Karen Roberts.

KT-427-225

Introduction

The Science Coordination Group has been set up with the aim of producing specialised revision material for National Curriculum Science.
This is one of a set of six books which provide concise coverage of the National Curriculum Key Stage 4 syllabus for *GCSE Double Science*.
They are ideally suited to all syllabuses produced by the main Examination Boards for GCSE Double Science, both Coordinated and Modular.

Throughout these books there is constant emphasis on the inescapable need to ***keep learning the basic facts***. This simple message is hammered home without compromise and without remorse, and whilst this traditionally brutal philosophy may not be quite in line with some other approaches to education, we still rather like it. But only because it works.

Contents

Section One — Plants

Life Processes and Cells 1
Specialised Plant Cells 2
Diffusion 3
Diffusion Through Cell Membranes 4
Basic Plant Structure 5
Leaf Structure 6
The Transpiration Stream 7
Transport Systems in Plants 8
Photosynthesis 9
Photosynthesis and Respiration 10
Altering the Rate of Photosynthesis 12
The Photosynthesis Experiment 13
How Plants Use The Glucose 14
Water Uptake and Essential Minerals 15
Growth Hormones in Plants 16
Commercial Use of Plant Hormones 17
Revision Summary For Section One 18

Section Two — Human Biology I

Nutrition 19
The Digestive System 20
Digestive Enzymes 21
Teeth 22
Muscular and Glandular Tissue 23
Diffusion of "Food" Molecules 24
Nutrient Deficiencies and Food Tests 25
The Circulatory System 26
The Heart 27
The Pumping Cycle 28
Blood Vessels 29
Blood 30
Lungs and Breathing 31
Alveoli, Cells and Diffusion 32
Respiration 33
Anaerobic Respiration — You and Yeast 34
The Nervous System 35
The Central Nervous System 36
Neurones and Reflexes 37
The Eye 38
Revision Summary for Section Two 39

Section Three — Human Biology II

Hormones 40
Insulin and Diabetes 41
Female Menstrual Cycle 42
Hormones in the Menstrual Cycle 43
Disease in Humans 44
Fighting Disease 45
Drugs 46
Alcohol and Tobacco 47
Homeostasis 48
Organs Involved in Homeostasis 49
Kidneys 50
Control of Body Temperature 52
Revision Summary for Section Three 53

Section Four — Genetics and Evolution

Types of Creature 54
Using a Key To Identify Creatures 55
Variation in Plants and Animals 56
Human Reproduction 58
Fertilisation and The Embryo 59
Genes, Chromosomes and DNA 60
Fertilisation: Sperm and Egg Meet Up 61
Girl or Boy? — X and Y Chromosomes 62
Clones and Asexual Reproduction 63
Mutations 64
Cystic Fibrosis and Huntington's Chorea 66
Sickle Cell Anaemia and Haemophilia 67
Selective Breeding 68
Fossils 70
Evolution 72
Extinction 73
Revision Summary for Section Four 74

Section Five — Environment

Adapt and Survive 75
Prey and Predators 76
Population Sizes 77
Atmospheric Pollution 78
The Greenhouse Effect 79
Acid Rain 80
There's Too Many People 81
Problems Caused By Farming 82
Food Webs 84
Making Holes in Food Webs 85
Pyramids Of Number and Biomass 86
Decomposition and The Carbon Cycle 87
Revision Summary for Section Five 88

Index 89

Page References for Modular Syllabuses

NEAB Double Award Science — Modular Syllabus 1998

Module 1: Humans as Organisms ..... Pages: 1-4, 19-21, 23-24, 26-34, 44-45

Module 2: Maintenance of Life ..... Pages: 1-18, 35-36, 38, 40-41, 46-52

Module 3: Environment ..... Pages: 75-78, 80-87

Module 4: Inheritance and Selection ..... Pages: 42-43, 54-64, 66, 68-73

ULEAC Double Award Science — Modular Syllabus 1998

Module 1: Body Maintenance ..... Pages: 19-26, 30-31, 35-38, 40-41, 45-52, 67

Module 2: Inheritance and Survival ..... Pages: 1-2, 40, 42, 54-66, 68-73, 75-78, 80

Module 3: Understanding Ecosystems ..... Pages: 1-18, 79, 81-87

Module 7: Science in Sport ..... Pages: 26-29, 31-34
(The rest of this module is covered in the Physics Book.)

SEG Double Award Science — Modular Syllabus 1998

Module 1: Maintenance of Life ..... Pages: 1-2, 19-24, 26, 29-30, 35-41, 48-52

Module 2: Maintenance of The Species ..... Pages: 46-47, 54-64, 66-67, 70-73, 75-83

Module 6: Vital Exchanges ..... Pages: 1-18, 26-29, 31-34, 84-87
(A little of this module is covered in the Chemistry Book.)

Typesetting and Layout by The Science Coordination Group
Illustrations by: Sandy Gardner, e-mail: zimkit@aol.com
and Bowser, Colorado USA

Consultant Editor: Paddy Gannon BSc MA

Text, design, layout and illustrations © Richard Parsons 1997, 1998. All rights reserved
With thanks to CorelDRAW for providing one or two bits of jolly clipart

Printed by Hindson Print, Newcastle upon Tyne

Life Processes and Cells

The Seven Life Processes which show you're alive

There are seven things they call "*LIFE PROCESSES*", — things that *all plants and animals do*.
You should learn all seven well enough to write them down *from memory*.
Use the little jollyism "MRS NERG" to remind you of the first letter of each word.

M — Movement	Being able to *move* parts of the body.
R — Reproduction	Producing *offspring*.
S — Sensitivity	*Responding* to the outside world.
N — Nutrition	Getting *food* in where it's needed.
E — Excretion	*Getting rid* of waste products.
R — Respiration	Turning *food into energy*.
G — Growth	Getting to *adult size*.

(If you think about it, this list describes the entire life of a sheep — and a frighteningly large chunk of yours too.)

Plant Cells and Animal Cells Have Their Differences

You need to be able to draw these two cells *WITH ALL THE DETAILS* for each.

Animal Cell

Plant Cell

3 THINGS THEY BOTH HAVE IN COMMON:

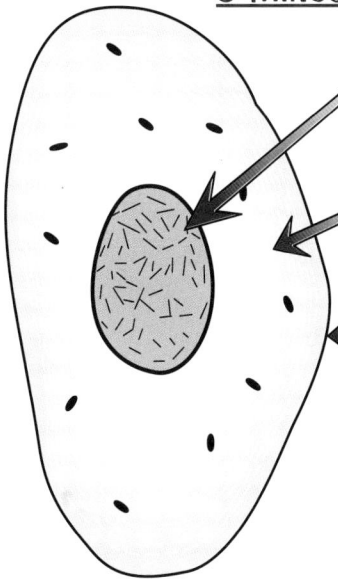

1) *NUCLEUS* controls what the cell *does*.

2) *CYTOPLASM* where the *chemical reactions* happen.

3) *CELL MEMBRANE* holds the cell together and *controls* what goes *in and out*.

3 EXTRAS THAT ONLY THE PLANT CELL HAS:

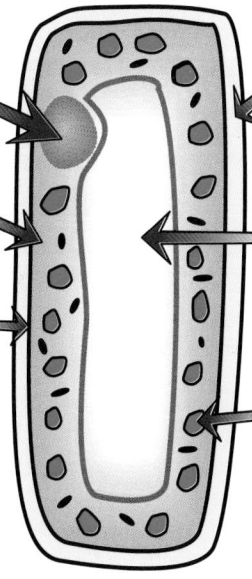

1) *RIGID CELL WALL* made of *cellulose*, gives *support* for the cell.

2) *VACUOLE* contains *cell sap*, a weak solution of sugar and salts.

3) *GREEN CHLOROPLASTS* containing *chlorophyll* for *photosynthesis*.

Have you learnt it? — let's see, shall we...

Right then, when you're ready, when you think you've learnt it, *cover the page* and *answer these*:

1) What are the 7 life processes, and what's the little jolly for remembering them?
2) Draw an animal cell and a plant cell and put all the labels on them.
3) What three things do plant and animal cells have in common?
4) What are the three differences between them?

Specialised Plant Cells

Most cells are ***SPECIALISED*** for a specific job, and in the Exam you'll probably have to explain why the cell they've shown you is so good at its job. It's a lot easier if you've *already learnt them*!

1) Palisade Leaf Cells are Designed for Photosynthesis

1) Packed with *chloroplasts* for *photosynthesis*.
2) *Tall shape* means a lot of *surface area* exposed down the side for *absorbing CO_2* from the air in the leaf.
3) Tall shape also means a good chance of *light* hitting a *chloroplast* before it reaches the bottom of the cell.

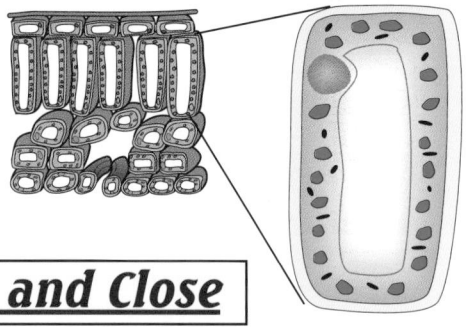

2) Guard Cells are Designed to Open and Close

1) Special *kidney shape* which *opens and closes* the stomata (a single pore is a "stoma") as the cells go *turgid* or *flaccid*.
2) *Thin* outer walls and *thickened* inner walls make this opening and closing function work properly.
3) They're also *sensitive to light* and *close at night* to conserve water without losing out on photosynthesis.

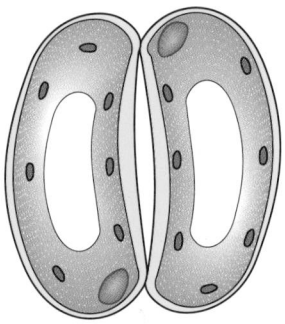

3) Three Other Important Examples:

There are three other important examples of specialised plant cells: *Root Hair cells* (P. 4), *Phloem cells* (P. 8) and *Xylem tubes* (P. 8). Look them up and see how they're specialised.

Cells, Tissues, Organs and Organ Systems

They like asking this in Exams, so learn the sequence:

A group of SIMILAR CELLS is called a TISSUE.
A group of DIFFERENT TISSUES form an ORGAN.
A GROUP OF ORGANS working together form an ORGAN SYSTEM, or even A WHOLE ORGANISM.

(This can apply to animals as well as plants, of course.)

A JOLLY EXAMPLE:

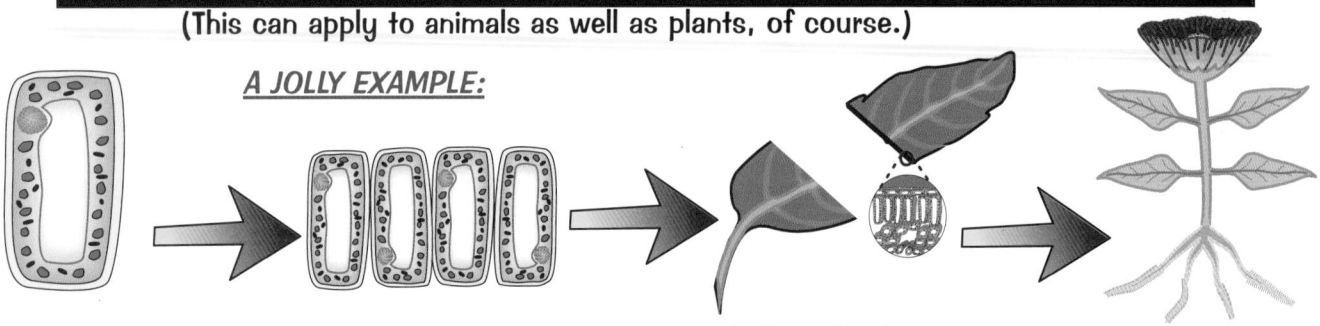

Palisade *CELLS*... ...make up palisade *TISSUE*... ...which, with other tissues make up a leaf (an *ORGAN*)... ...and leaves and other organs make up a full plant (an *ORGANISM*).

OK, let's see what you know...

When you think you've *LEARNT* everything on this page, *cover it up* and do these:
1) Sketch the five specialised cells on this page and point out their special features.
2) Give the full sequence from cells to organ-systems and sketch the example given above.

Diffusion

Don't be put off by the fancy word

"Diffusion" is really simple. It's just the *gradual movement of particles* from *places where there are lots of them* to places where there are *less of them*. That's all it is — ***IT'S JUST THE NATURAL TENDENCY FOR STUFF TO SPREAD OUT***.

Unfortunately you also have to ***LEARN*** the fancy way of saying the same thing, which is this:

DIFFUSION is the MOVEMENT OF PARTICLES from an area of HIGH CONCENTRATION to an area of LOW CONCENTRATION

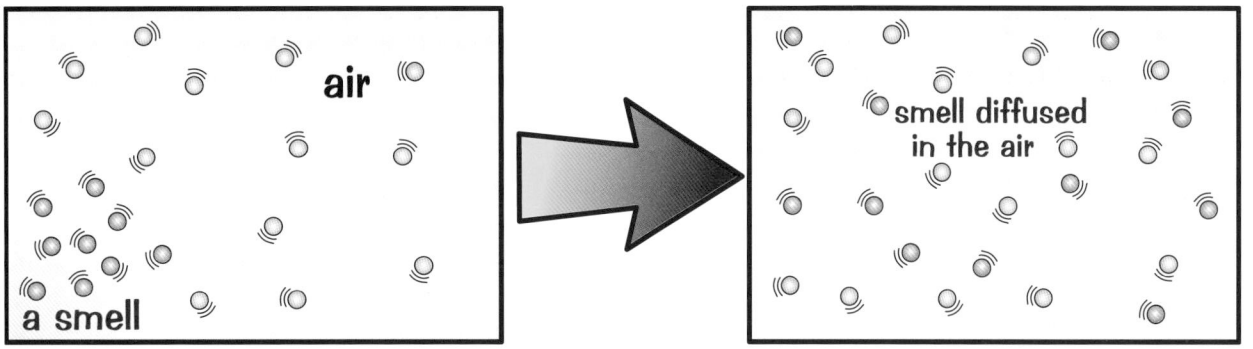

Diffusion of Gases in Leaves is vital for Photosynthesis

The *simplest type* of diffusion is where *different gases diffuse through each other*, like when a weird smell spreads out through the air in a room. Diffusion of gases also happens in *leaves* and they'll very likely put it in your Exam. *So learn it now*:

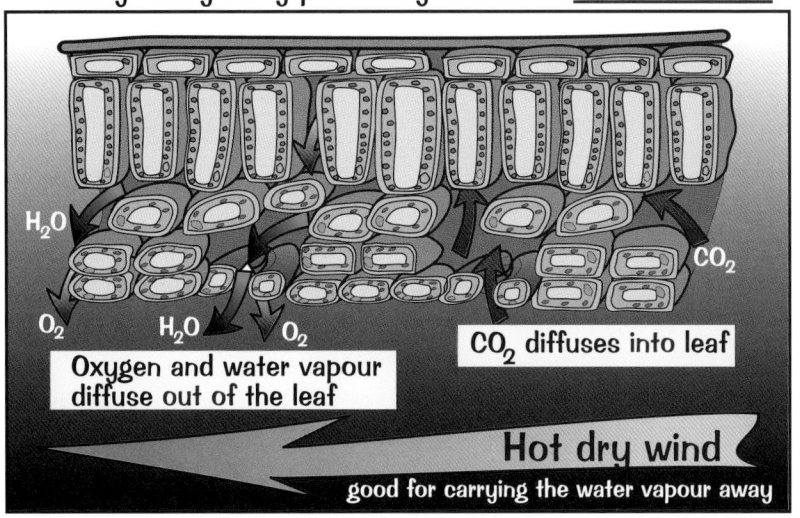

For ***PHOTOSYNTHESIS*** to happen, *carbon dioxide* gas has to get *inside the leaves*.

It does this by ***DIFFUSION*** through the biddy little holes under the leaf called *stomata*.

At the same time *water vapour* and *oxygen* diffuse *out* through the same biddy little holes.

The water vapour escapes by *diffusion* because *there's a lot of it inside the leaf* and *less of it in the air outside*. *This diffusion causes* ***TRANSPIRATION*** *and it goes quicker* when the air around the leaf is kept ***DRY*** — i.e. transpiration is quickest in ***HOT, DRY, WINDY CONDITIONS*** — and don't you forget it!

So, how much do you know about diffusion?

Yeah sure it's a pretty book but actually the big idea is to learn all the stuff that's in it.
So learn this page until you can answer these questions *without having to look back*:

1) Write down the fancy definition for diffusion, and then say what it means in your own words.
2) Draw the cross-section of the leaf with arrows to show which way the three gases diffuse.
3) What weather conditions make the diffusion of water vapour out of the leaf go fastest?

Diffusion Through Cell Membranes

Cell membranes are kind of clever...

They're kind of clever because they hold everything *inside* the cell, ***BUT***, they let stuff *in and out* as well. Only very *small molecules* can diffuse through cell membranes though — things like *glucose* or *amino acids*.

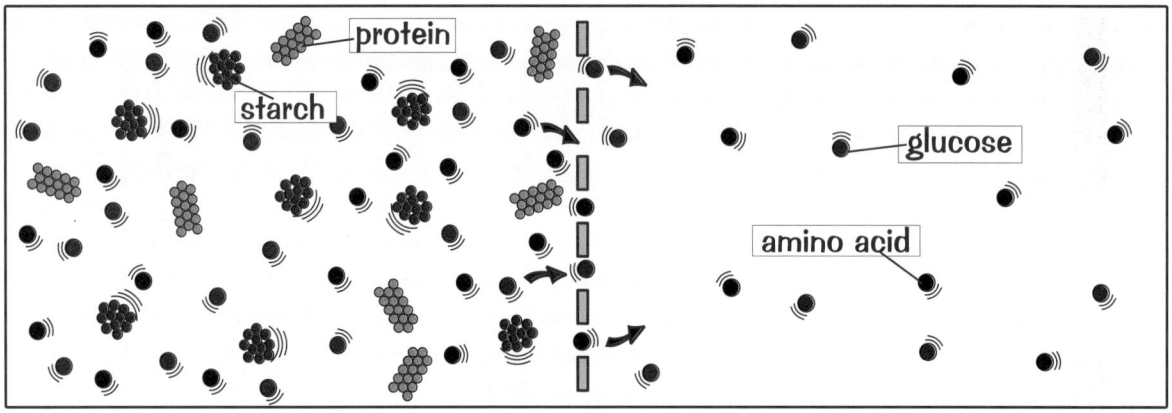

1) Notice that ***BIG MOLECULES*** like ***STARCH*** or ***PROTEINS*** can't diffuse through cell membranes — they could quite cheerfully ask you exactly that in the Exam.
2) Just like with diffusion in air, particles flow through the cell membrane from where there's a ***HIGH CONCENTRATION*** (a lot of them) to where there's a ***LOW CONCENTRATION*** (not such a lot of them).

Root Hairs take in Minerals and Water

1) The cells on plant roots grow into long "*hairs*" which stick out into the soil.
2) This gives the plant a *big surface area* for absorbing *water and minerals* from the soil.

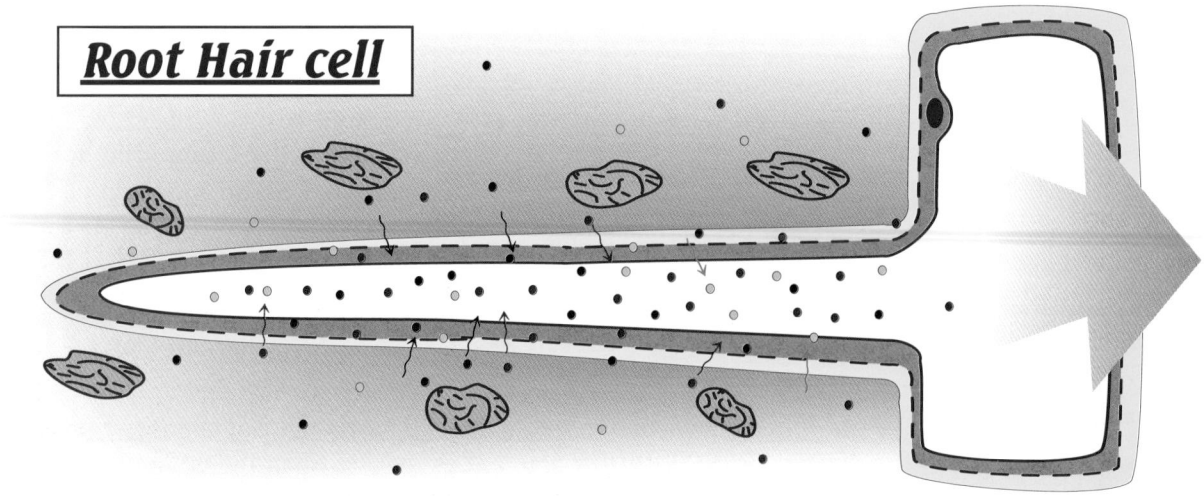

A Real Easy Page to Learn...

Make sure you can do these with the page covered up — if you can't, you ain't learnt nothin':

1) What type of molecule *will* diffuse through cell membranes and what type *won't*?
2) Give two examples of each.
3) Draw a full diagram of a root hair and say what it does.

Basic Plant Structure

You have to know all these parts of the plant and what they do:

The Five Different Bits of a Plant all do Different Jobs

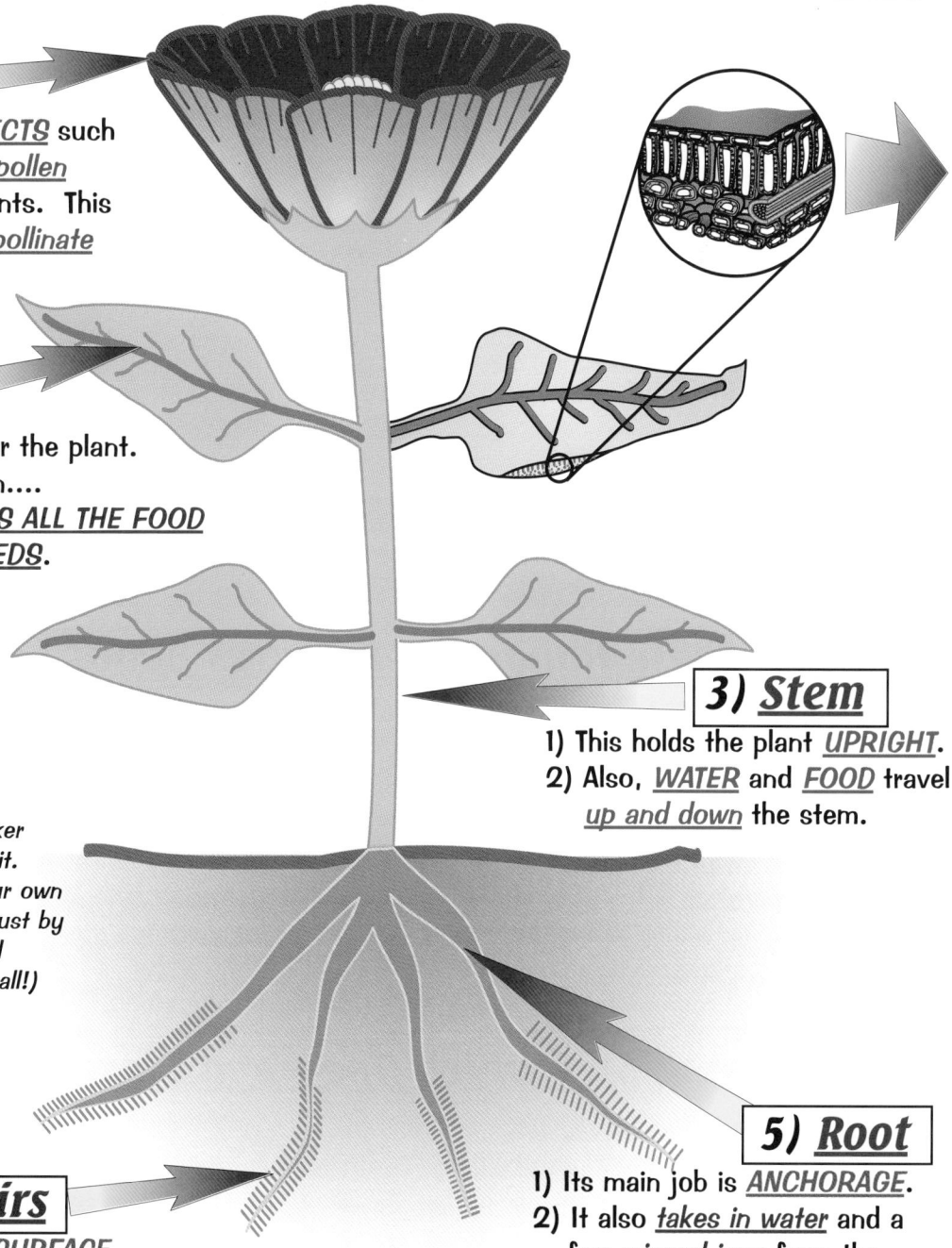

1) Flower

THIS ATTRACTS INSECTS such as bees which carry pollen between different plants. This allows the plants to pollinate and reproduce.

2) Leaf

It produces FOOD for the plant. I'll say it again, listen.... THE LEAF PRODUCES ALL THE FOOD THAT THE PLANT NEEDS.

Plants do not take food from the soil. Plants make all their own food in their leaves using PHOTOSYNTHESIS.

(That's a bit of a shocker when you think about it. Imagine making all your own food under your skin just by lying in the sun — and never having to eat at all!)

3) Stem

1) This holds the plant UPRIGHT.
2) Also, WATER and FOOD travel up and down the stem.

4) Root hairs

These give A BIG SURFACE AREA to absorb water and ions from the soil.

5) Root

1) Its main job is ANCHORAGE.
2) It also takes in water and a few mineral ions from the soil. But mostly just water. REMEMBER, plants do NOT take "food" in from the soil.

The Big Idea is to LEARN All That...

Everything on this page is there to be LEARNT because it's very likely to come up in your Exams. This is pretty basic stuff, but it can still catch you out if you don't learn it properly. For example: "What is the main function of the root?". Too many people answer that with "Taking food in from the soil" — Eeek! LEARN these facts. They all count. They're all worth marks in the Exam. Practise until you can sketch the diagram and scribble down ALL the details, without looking back.

Leaf Structure

Leaves are Designed for One Thing Only...

— Making Food by Photosynthesis

The whole structure of leaves is geared towards that. Make sure you learn this diagram with all its labels:

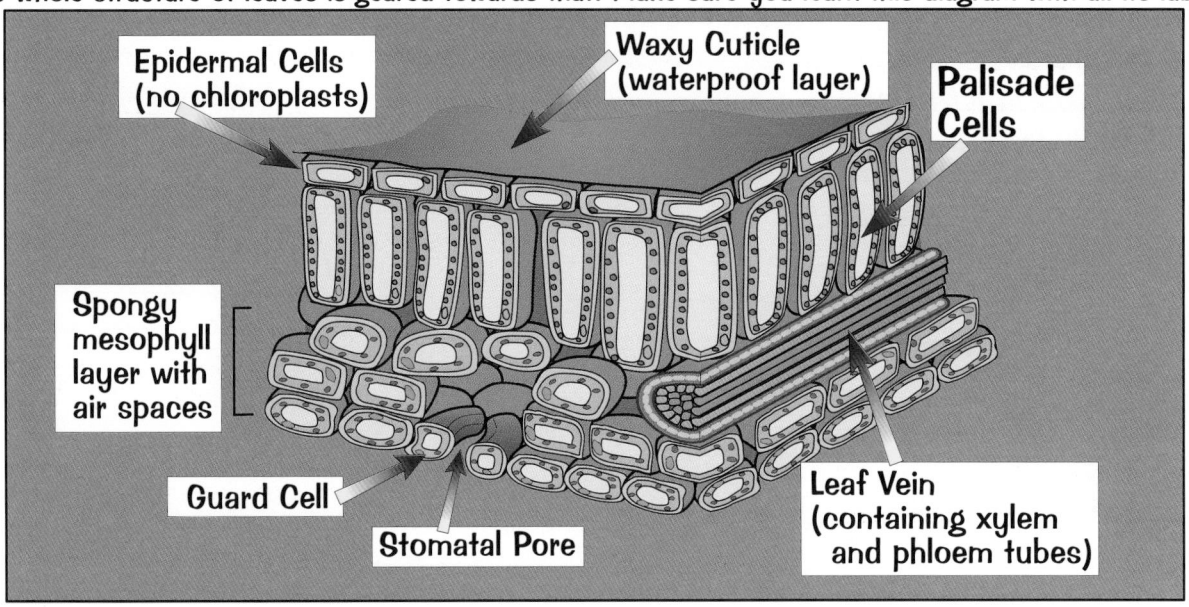

Learn all these Important Features about Leaves

1) The cells in the *palisade layer* are packed with *chloroplasts* which contain lots of *chlorophyll*. This is where the *photosynthesis* goes on.
2) The *palisade* and *spongy layers* are full of *air spaces* to allow CO_2 to reach the palisade cells.
3) The cells in the *epidermis* make *wax* which covers the *leaf surface*, especially the *top surface*. This is to *prevent water loss*.
4) The *lower surface* is full of biddy little holes called *stomata*. They are there to *let CO_2 in*. They also allow water to escape — this is how the *transpiration stream* comes about.
5) *Xylem* and *phloem* vessels cover the whole leaf like tiny "*veins*", to *deliver water* to every part of the leaf and then to *take away the food* (starch) produced by the leaf.

Stomata are Pores which Open and Close Automatically

1) *Stomata* close *automatically* when supplies of water from the roots start to *dry up*.
2) The *guard cells* control this. When water is *scarce*, they become *flaccid*, and they change shape, which *closes* the stomatal pores.
3) This *prevents* any more water being *lost*, but also stops CO_2 getting in, so the photosynthesis stops as well.

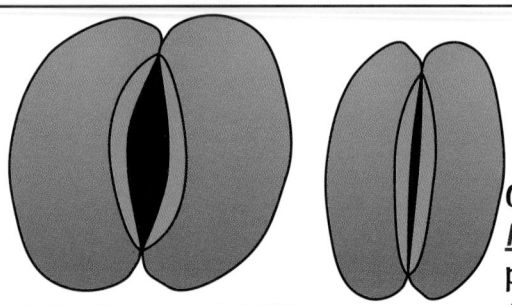

Cells *TURGID*, pore *OPENS*

Cells *FLACCID*, pore *CLOSES*

Spend some time poring over these facts...

Two spiffing diagrams and a few simple features. What could be easier? Check the clock and give yourself five minutes of intense active learning to see how much you can learn. "*Intense active learning*" means *covering the page* and *scribbling down* the details, but don't take 5 minutes drawing out a neat diagram of a leaf — that's just a waste of precious time.

The Transpiration Stream

Transpiration is the loss of water from the Plant

1) It's caused by the *evaporation* of water from *inside the leaves*.
2) This creates a *slight shortage* of water in the leaf which *draws more water up* from the rest of the plant which *in turn* draws more up from the *roots*.
3) It has *two beneficial effects*: a) it *transports minerals* from the soil b) it *cools* the plant.

4 Factors which affect it

The *rate of transpiration* is affected by *four things*:

1) Amount of *light*.
2) *Temperature*.
3) Amount of *air movement*.
4) *Humidity* of the surrounding air.

It's surely obvious that the *biggest* rate of transpiration occurs in *hot*, *dry*, *windy*, *sunny* conditions i.e. perfect clothes-drying weather.

By contrast, a *cool*, *cloudy*, *muggy*, *miserable day* with *no wind* will produce *minimum transpiration*.

This constant stream of water has the advantage of transporting *vital minerals* from the *SOIL* into the roots and then all around the plant.

The uptake of *WATER* and *MINERALS* happens almost entirely at the *ROOT HAIRS*.

Turgor Pressure Supports Plant Tissues

1) When a plant is *well watered*, all its cells will draw water into themselves and become *turgid*, which just means "*bloated*".
2) The contents of the cell start to *push against the cell wall*, kind of like a balloon in a shoebox, and thereby give *support* to the plant tissues. This is called *turgor pressure*.
3) *Leaves* are *entirely supported* by this *turgor pressure*. We know this because if there's no water in the soil, a plant starts to *wilt* and the leaves *droop*. This is because the cells start to lose water and thus lose their turgor pressure.

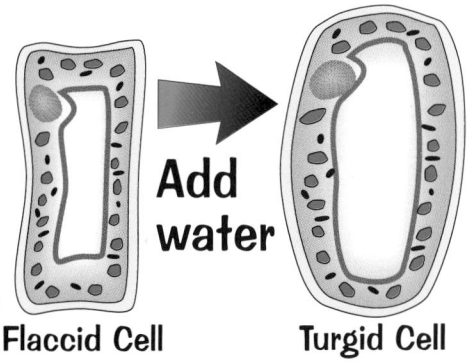

It helps if you're quick on the uptake...

There's quite a lot of information on this page. You could try learning the numbered points, but you'll find a better plan is to do a "*mini-essay*" on transpiration and write down everything you can think of. Then look back to see what you've forgotten. Then do it again! *Till you get it all*.

Transport Systems in Plants

Plants need to transport various things around inside themselves. They have tubes for it.

Phloem and Xylem Vessels Transport Different Things

1) Plants have two separate sets of tubes for transporting stuff around the plant.
2) Both sets of tubes go to every part of the plant, but they are totally separate.
3) They usually run alongside each other.

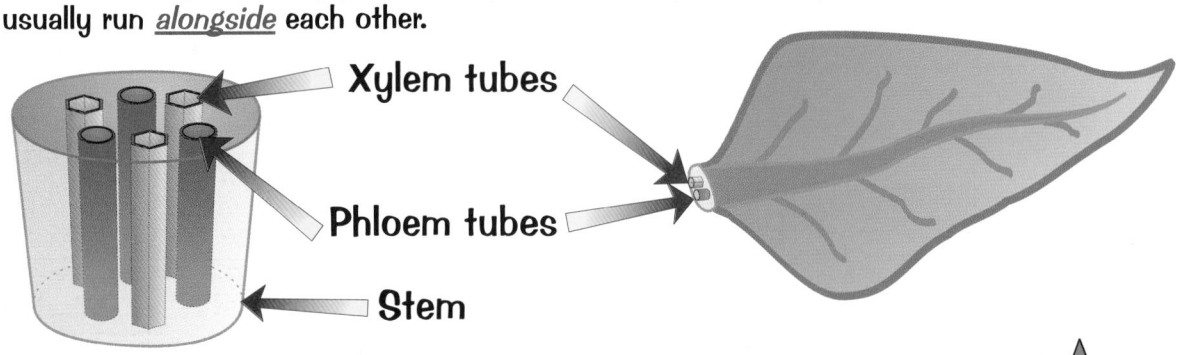

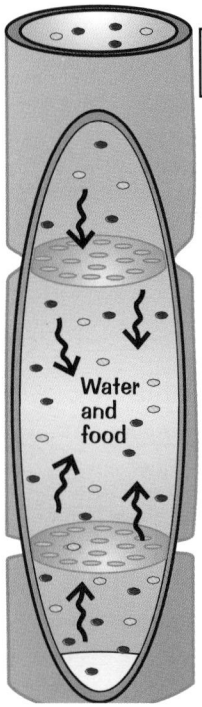

Phloem Tubes transport Food:

1) Made of living cells with perforated end-plates to allow stuff to flow through.
2) They transport food made in the leaves to all other parts of the plant, in both directions.
3) They carry sugars, fats, proteins etc. to growing regions in shoot tips and root tips and to/from storage organs in the roots.

Xylem Tubes take water UP:

1) Made of dead cells joined end to end with no end walls between them.
2) The side walls are strong and stiff and contain lignin. This gives the plant support.
3) They carry water and minerals from the roots up to the leaves in the transpiration stream.

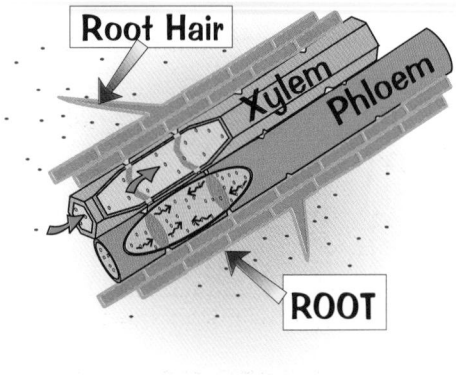

The Phloem and Xylem extend into the Roots

1) The phloem carries starch down to the roots for growth or for storage and may later carry it back up again.
2) The xylem carries water and minerals (which are taken in by the roots) up to the leaves.

Well that seems to be about the top and bottom of it...

This is an easy page. There are important differences between xylem and phloem tubes. Make sure you know all the numbered points on this page, and the diagrams. Then cover the page and scribble it all down with detailed sketches of the diagrams. Then do it again, until you get it all.

Photosynthesis

Photosynthesis Produces Glucose from Sunlight

1) *Photosynthesis* is the process that *produces "food"* in plants. The "food" it produces is *glucose*.
2) Photosynthesis *takes place* in the *leaves* of all *green plants* — this is what leaves *are for*.

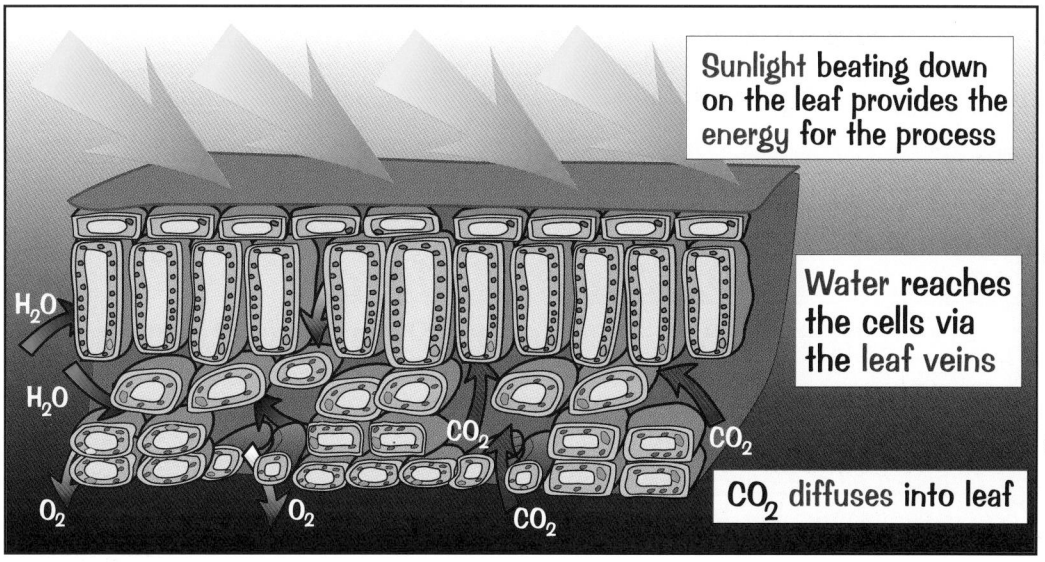

THREE FEATURES:

1) Leaves are *thin and flat* to provide a *big surface area* to catch *lots* of sunlight.
2) The *palisade* cells are *near the top* of the leaf and are *packed with chloroplasts*.
3) *Guard cells* control the *movement of gases* into and out of the leaf through the *stomata*.

Learn the Equation for Photosynthesis:

CARBON DIOXIDE + WATER $\xrightarrow[\text{chlorophyll}]{\text{SUNLIGHT}}$ GLUCOSE + OXYGEN

Four Things are Needed for Photosynthesis to Happen:

1) Light

Usually from the *SUN*.

2) Chlorophyll

The *green substance* which is found in *chloroplasts* and which makes leaves look *green*.

This is the "magic" stuff that makes it all happen. Chlorophyll *absorbs the energy in sunlight* and uses it to combine *CO_2* and *WATER* to produce *GLUCOSE*. Oxygen is simply a by-product.

3) Carbon dioxide

Enters the leaf from the *AIR* around.

4) Water

Comes *FROM THE SOIL*, up the stem and into the leaf.

Live and Learn...

What you've got to do now is learn everything on this page. Photosynthesis is a "dead cert" for the Exams. On this page you've got two diagrams, two points about photosynthesis and the equations, and then the four necessary conditions. Just *keep learning them* until you can *cover the page* and write them all down *from memory*. Only then will you really *know it all*.

Photosynthesis and Respiration

Photosynthesis and Respiration are OPPOSITE Processes:

You need to realise the close connection between photosynthesis and respiration. Read on...

Photosynthesis in Plants Provides the Food for All Life

1) Remember that photosynthesis in plants provides the food for all animals.
2) Plants trap the Sun's energy and turn it into glucose, which is basically stored chemical energy.
3) Animals along the food chain then use that energy in respiration to live and grow.
So without plants to make the food in the first place (by photosynthesis), all animals would die.

Respiration uses up the Oxygen and Glucose which was made by Photosynthesis

1) Respiration uses up oxygen and glucose and turns it back into carbon dioxide and water.
2) Both animals and plants do respiration all the time.
Respiration is what provides all the energy for living.
All the seven life processes (remember MRS NERG — see P. 1) need energy for them to happen and it's respiration which provides that energy.
3) On Earth we have lots of plants doing lots of photosynthesis which uses up carbon dioxide and produces oxygen and glucose.
4) At the same time there are lots of plants and animals doing respiration and using up oxygen and giving out carbon dioxide.

The EQUATIONS are the same but in opposite directions:

The Equation for Photosynthesis

CARBON DIOXIDE + WATER → GLUCOSE + OXYGEN

(Requires Energy)

In photosynthesis, energy from the sun is used to combine carbon dioxide and water to produce glucose (and oxygen as a by-product). This process takes in energy and stores it.

The Equation for Respiration

GLUCOSE + OXYGEN → CARBON DIOXIDE + WATER

(Energy released)

In respiration, energy is released. This energy originally came from the sun. It was stored by the plant when it did photosynthesis. That's when the glucose was produced in the first place.

Photosynthesis — where would we be without it...

It's pretty handy if you can get it into your head that photosynthesis provides all the food and oxygen for all living things to thrive on. Respiration is the opposite process which uses up the food and oxygen. Learn the whole page, including the two equations, then cover it up and scribble it all down. Keep practising until you can remember it all. Enjoy.

Photosynthesis and Respiration

Enclosed Plants: O_2 and CO_2 monitored over 24 hour cycles

1) In *daylight* (or any other light) plants do *photosynthesis* and produce *oxygen* (and glucose).
2) But *both plants and animals* do *respiration* all the time, day and night, which uses up the oxygen and *releases* carbon dioxide.
3) A mildly interesting *experiment* can be done to demonstrate this happening:

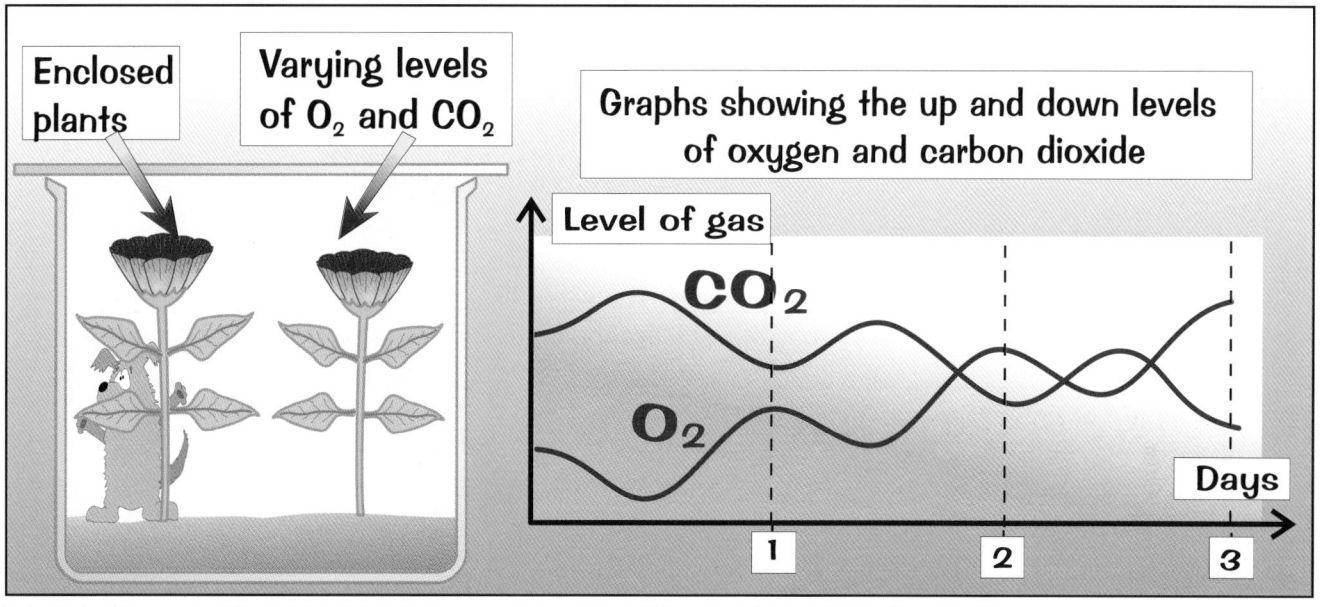

Make Sure you Get the Grip of This Experiment

1) The level of *oxygen* will *rise* in the *daytime* due to *photosynthesis* producing more *oxygen* than the plant's respiration uses up.
2) *At night* the level of oxygen will *fall* because the plant's *respiration* will use it up, and none is being produced.
3) However, *over a period of time* the level of oxygen will *slowly rise*.
4) The level of *carbon dioxide* will *fall* during in the *daytime* (used up by photosynthesis) and will *rise* at *night* (produced by respiration).
5) Over a period of time the level of CO_2 will *fall steadily* because plants obviously *use up* more CO_2 than they *produce*. (Otherwise our atmosphere would still be full of carbon dioxide like it was billions of years ago.)

Animals in there too could make the CO_2 level rise

1) It depends on the *relative sizes* of the *plants and animals* of course, but basically over a period of time the level of O_2 could now *fall*, and the level of CO_2 could *rise* if there's too much "animal" compared to "plant".
2) This is because the plant and animal between them could be using up more oxygen than the plant is managing to produce by photosynthesis in the daylight period.
3) The *24 hour pattern* of *up and down* would still be similar though.

How do you learn all that lot then?...

Learn how the levels of oxygen and carbon dioxide vary over periods of 24 hours or longer for an enclosed plant with or without animals in there with it.
Make sure you remember which one rises at night and which one rises in the daytime.
Then *cover the page* and try to *scribble it all down*. It's really not that difficult.

Altering the Rate of Photosynthesis

The Rate of Photosynthesis depends on Three Factors

The RATE of photosynthesis is affected by these THREE FACTORS:

1) THE AMOUNT OF LIGHT

The chlorophyll uses light energy to perform photosynthesis. It can only do it as fast as the light energy is arriving.

2) THE AMOUNT OF CARBON DIOXIDE

CO_2 and water are the raw materials. Water is never really in short supply in a plant but only 0.03% of the air around is CO_2 so it's actually pretty scarce as far as plants are concerned.

3) THE TEMPERATURE

Chlorophyll is an ENZYME so it works best when it's warm but not too hot. The rate of photosynthesis depends on how "happy" the chlorophyll enzyme is: WARM but not too hot.

The More of those Three Things, the Faster it Grows

Remember, a plant has to do photosynthesis to make the glucose which allows it to grow. To get the best rate of photosynthesis (and growth) you need to make sure that:

1) There's enough carbon dioxide
2) There's plenty of light
3) The temperature is high enough

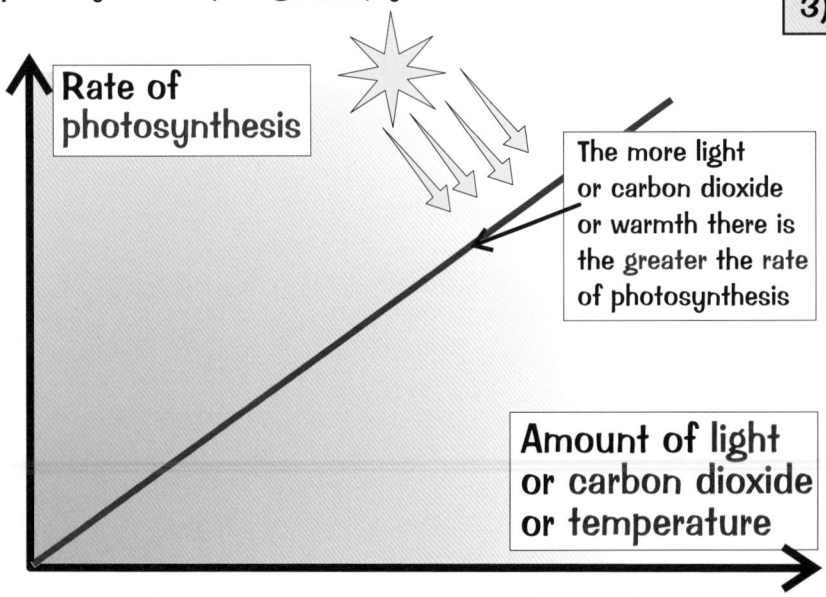

In tropical countries they have lots of warmth and light which is why the tropical rainforests grow so quickly.

In this country we only have enough warmth and light in the summer.

In winter it's too cold for photosynthesis and so plants don't grow any bigger in the winter. They just tough it out and survive till spring and then start growing again.

The Temperature can get Too Hot if You're not Careful

1) You can't really have too much light or carbon dioxide.
2) The temperature on the other hand mustn't get too high or it destroys the chlorophyll enzymes. This happens at about 45°C.
   That's pretty hot for outdoors, though greenhouses can get that hot if you're not careful.
3) Usually, though, the temperature is too low, and things need warming up a bit to get the photosynthesis working faster.

Revision — life isn't all fun and sunshine...

There are three factors which affect how quickly plants do photosynthesis, which affects how quickly they grow. Cover the page and practise learning all these details, until you can do it.

The Photosynthesis Experiment

This is a particularly jolly leaf experiment which they're quite likely to test in your Exams:

1) Photosynthesis and the Starch Test

(Another sixties pop group — or maybe not.)

1) This is a *real simple experiment* to find out what affects *starch production* in a leaf. If starch is being produced it means that *photosynthesis* is going on. The answer of course is that *light* and *carbon dioxide* are what affect it.

2) All the experiment does is *deprive* parts of a leaf of either *light* or *carbon dioxide* for 24 hours or so and then *test for starch* using *iodine*.

3) Mind you there are quite a few picky details you need to know about for when they ask you in the Exam, so *learn all these steps*:

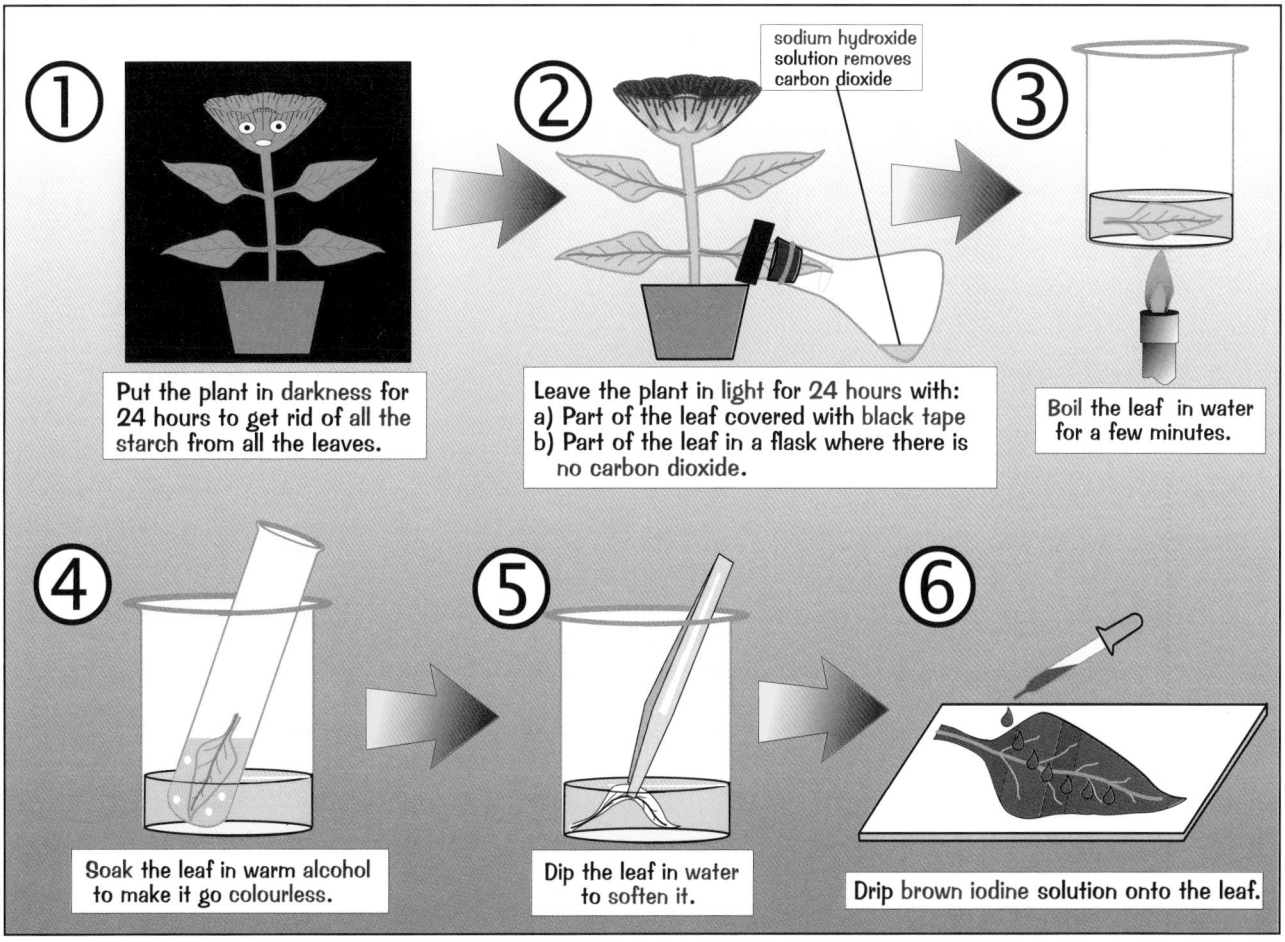

4) If the *iodine* goes *dark blue/black* then *starch is present*, showing *that bit of leaf* was managing to do *photosynthesis*.

5) If the iodine *stays brown* then there's *no starch*, which shows that part of the leaf was *NOT* managing to do photosynthesis — because it *wasn't getting* either *light* or *CO_2*.

6) It should be *obvious* that the bit of leaf that was covered in *black tape* (no light), and the bit of leaf in the *flask* (no carbon dioxide), will both have *no starch* in them.

Starch Production — this should shed some light on it...

This experiment is quite a good one for Exam questions, so try and learn all the steps and what they're needed for. The most important thing you need to realise is that the leaf is deprived of light or carbon dioxide just to prove they are needed for photosynthesis. *Learn and scribble*.

How Plants Use The Glucose

1) Plants *manufacture glucose* in their *leaves*.
2) They then use some of the glucose initially for *respiration*.
3) This *releases energy* which enables them to *convert* the rest of the glucose into various *other useful substances* which they can use to *build new cells* and *grow*.
4) To produce some of these substances they also need to *gather* a few *minerals* from the soil.

For Respiration ①

Making Fruits ②

GLUCOSE is turned into *SUCROSE* for storing in *FRUITS*.
Fruits deliberately *taste nice* so that animals will eat them and so *spread the seeds* all over the place.

③ Making Cell walls

GLUCOSE is converted into *CELLULOSE* for making *cell walls*.

④ Stored as Starch

Glucose is turned into *starch* and *stored* in roots, stems and leaves, ready for use when photosynthesis isn't happening, like in the *winter*.

⑤ Making Proteins

GLUCOSE is combined with *NITRATES* (collected from the *soil*) to make *AMINO ACIDS*, which are then made into *PROTEINS*.

Starch is Insoluble — better for storing than glucose

STARCH is *INSOLUBLE* which makes it much *better* than glucose for *storing*.
Potato and carrot plants store a lot of *starch* in their *roots* over the winter to enable a new plant to grow from it the following spring. *We eat the swollen roots*!

"Sugar it", that's what I say...

There are five things that plants do with glucose. Can you spot them? If so, *learn them*, *cover the page*, and then display your new-found knowledge. In other words, sketch out the diagram and *scribble down* the five ways that plants use glucose, including all the extra details.

Water Uptake and Essential Minerals

Testing Water uptake With a Potometer

1) This experiment tests the *rate of water uptake* of a plant in different *atmospheric conditions*.
2) As water *evaporates* from the leaves, it *draws it up* the stem and the *bubble* moves along the tube.

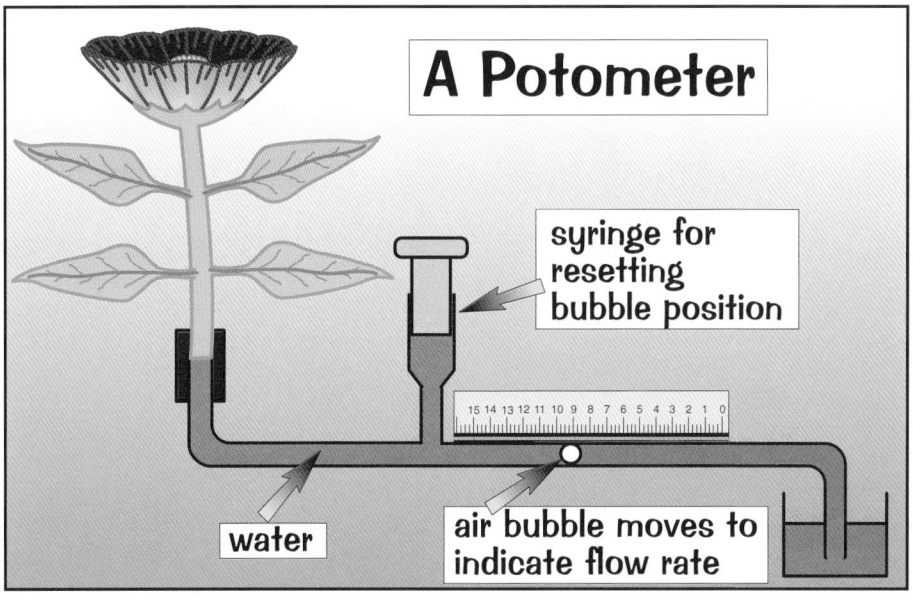

3) The *further* the bubble travels in a given time, the *faster* the rate of *water uptake*.

4) So this is a good way to measure the rate of *transpiration*.

5) You can expose the plant to *wind* or *heat* or *moisture* etc., to see how it affects the rate of water uptake.

Plants need Nitrates, Iron and Magnesium

For *healthy growth* plants need these really important minerals which they can only obtain *from the soil* through their *roots*:

1) Nitrates are Needed for making Plant Protein

Nitrates are needed for making *AMINO ACIDS* and for the "synthesis" (making) of *PROTEINS*.

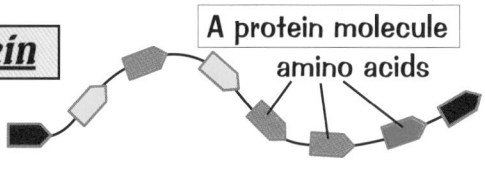

2) Iron and Magnesium are needed for making Chlorophyll

IRON and *MAGNESIUM* are needed for making *CHLOROPHYLL*, which is pretty important to plants, in case you didn't know.

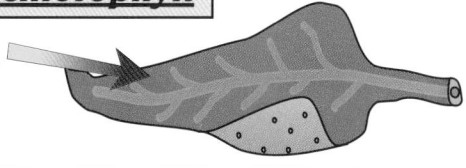

The Perils of Monoculture

1) *Monoculture* is where *JUST ONE TYPE OF CROP* is grown in the same field *year after year*.
2) This causes the soil to become *deficient in the minerals* which that *particular plant uses* lots of.
3) *Deficiency* of just *one mineral* is enough to cause *poor growth and reduced yield*.
4) This soon results in poor crops unless *fertiliser* is added to *replenish* the depleted minerals.

Test Yourself Here to find out what you've taken in...

A simple experiment that you need to be familiar with, and three essential minerals that plants need for healthy growth. Make sure you know all about them. Also learn what "monoculture" means and why it's not always too clever. Practise with the *scribbled "mini-essay" method*.

Growth Hormones in Plants

Auxins are Plant Growth Hormones

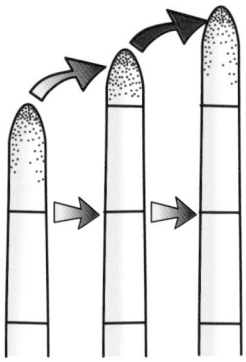

1) Auxins are hormones which control growth at the tips of shoots and roots.
2) Auxin is produced in the tips and diffuses backwards to stimulate the cell elongation process which occurs in the cells just behind the tips.
3) If the tip of a shoot is removed, no auxin will be available and the shoot may stop growing.
4) Shoot tips also produce substances which inhibit the growth of side shoots. If the tips are removed it can result in a lot of side shoots because the inhibitor substance is no longer present. Hence, hedge clipping promotes bushier hedges, because it produces lots of side shoots.

Auxins Change The Direction of Root and Shoot Growth

You'll note below that extra auxin promotes growth in the shoot but actually inhibits growth in the root — but also note that this produces the desired result in both cases.

1) Shoots bend towards the light

1) When a shoot tip is exposed to light, it provides more auxin on the side that is in the shade than the side which is in the light.
2) This causes the shoot to grow faster on the shaded side and it bends towards the light.

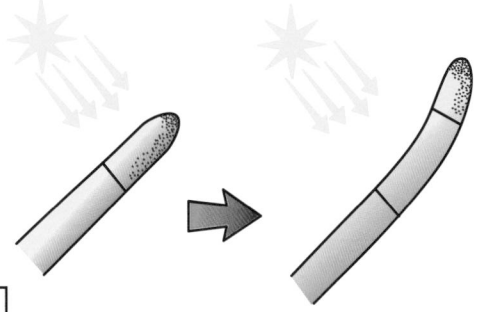

2) Shoots bend away from Gravity

1) When a shoot finds itself growing sideways, the gravity produces an unequal distribution of auxin in the tip, with more auxin on the lower side.
2) This causes the lower side to grow faster, thus bending the shoot upwards.

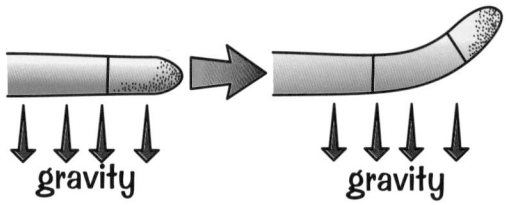

3) Roots bend towards Gravity

1) A root growing sideways will experience the same redistribution of auxin to the lower side.
2) But in a root the extra auxin actually inhibits growth, causing it to bend downwards instead.

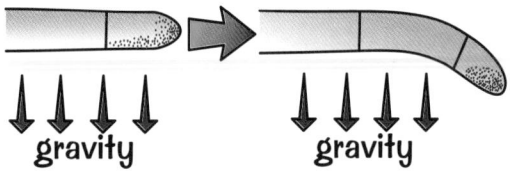

4) Roots bend towards Moisture

1) An uneven degree of moisture either side of a root will cause more auxin to appear on the side with more moisture.
2) This inhibits growth on that side, causing the root to grow in that direction, towards the moisture.

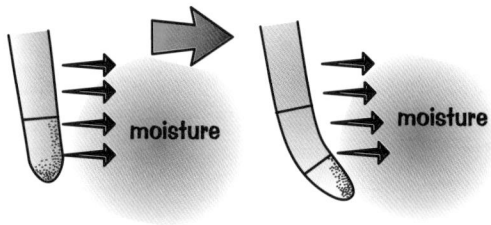

Just A Few Tips for Your Revision...

An easy page to learn. Just four points on auxins, together with a diagram, and then four ways that shoots and roots change direction, with a diagram for each. You just have to learn it. Then cover the page and scribble down the main points from memory. Then try again, and again...

Commercial Use of Plant Hormones

Plant hormones have a lot of uses in the food growing business.

1) Producing Seedless Fruit

1) Fruits normally only grow on plants which have been pollinated by insects, with the inevitable seeds in the middle of the fruit. If the plant doesn't get pollinated, the fruits and seeds don't grow.
2) However, if growth hormones are applied to unpollinated flowers the fruits will grow but the seeds won't!
3) This is great. Seedless satsumas and seedless grapes are just so much nicer than the "natural" ones full of pips!

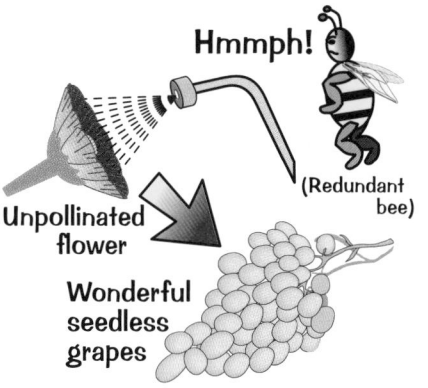

2) Controlling the Ripening of Fruit

1) The ripening of fruits can be controlled either while they are still on the plant, or during transport to the shops.
2) This allows the fruit to be picked while it's still unripe (and therefore firmer and less easily damaged).
3) It can then be sprayed with ripening hormone and it will ripen on the way to the supermarket to be perfect just as it reaches the shelves.

3) Growing from Cuttings with Rooting Compound

1) A cutting is part of a plant that has been cut off it, like the end of a branch with a few leaves on it.
2) Normally, if you stick cuttings in the soil they won't grow, but if you add rooting compound, which is a plant growth hormone, they will produce roots rapidly and start growing as new plants.
3) This enables growers to produce lots of clones (exact copies) of a really good plant very quickly.

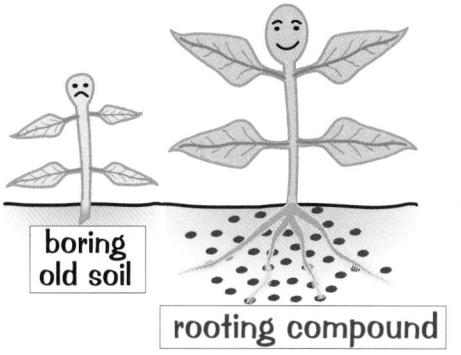

4) Killing Weeds

1) Most weeds growing in fields of crops or in a lawn are broad-leaved, in contrast to grass which has very narrow leaves.
2) Selective weedkillers have been developed from plant growth hormones which only affect the broad-leaved plants.
3) They totally disrupt their normal growth patterns, which soon kills them, whilst leaving the grass untouched.

Remember, serious learning always bears fruit...

Another blissfully easy page. Just make sure you learn enough about each bit to answer a 3 mark Exam question on it (that means being able to make 3 valid points). As usual the sections are split into numbered points to help you remember them. They've all got three points to learn. So learn them. Then cover the page and scribble down the 3 points for each. And tell me this: — if you can't do it now, what makes you think it'll all suddenly *"come back to you"* in the Exam?

Revision Summary For Section One

There's a lot of real easy stuff on plants, that's for sure. But easy stuff means easy marks, and you better make sure you get all the easy marks — every last one. There's nothing quite as spectacularly dumb as working really hard at the difficult stuff and then forgetting about the easy bits. Here's some tough questions on plants for you. Practise them over and over and over until you can just glide through them all, like a swan or something.

1) What use is Mrs Nerg?
2) Sketch an animal cell and a plant cell with the six labels.
3) Sketch a palisade leaf cell and explain how they're specialised for their job.
4) Sketch a pair of guard cells and explain how they're specialised for their job.
5) Name three other plant cells which are specialised for their job.
6) Give an example of this sequence: cells → tissues → organ → organism.
7) Give the strict definition of diffusion. Sketch how a smell diffuses through air in a room.
8) Which three gases diffuse in and out of leaves? What process are they involved with?
9) Why are cell membranes kinda clever? What will and won't diffuse through cell membranes?
10) Draw a diagram of a root hair cell.
11) What happens at root hairs? What things are taken in?
12) Sketch a typical plant and label the five important parts. Explain exactly what each bit does.
13) Sketch the cross-section of a leaf with seven labels. What is the leaf for?
14) Give five written details about the leaf structure in relation to what the leaf needs to do.
15) Explain what stomata do and how they do it.
16) What is transpiration? What causes it? What benefits does it bring?
17) What are the four factors which affect the rate of transpiration?
18) What is turgor pressure? How does it come about and what use is it to plants?
19) What are the two types of tubes in plants? Whereabouts are they found in plants?
20) List three features for both types of tube and sketch them both.
21) Sketch a root and say what goes on in the tubes inside it.
22) What does photosynthesis do? Where does it do it?
23) Write down the equation for photosynthesis.
24) Sketch a leaf and show the four things needed for photosynthesis.
25) What is the relationship between photosynthesis and respiration?
26) Write down the two equations, and say which way the energy goes in each one.
27) Describe an experiment to demonstrate the effects of photosynthesis and respiration. Sketch the graphs and explain their shape. What is the effect of animals?
28) What three things affect the rate of photosynthesis in a plant?
29) Sketch a graph to show how the rate of photosynthesis varies with each of these three.
30) Describe conditions where each of these three factors is in short supply.
31) Describe the six stages of an experiment to demonstrate when photosynthesis will happen.
32) What is the test for starch?
33) Sketch a plant and label the five ways that plants use glucose.
34) Give a couple of extra details for each of the five uses.
35) Sketch a potometer and explain what it can be used to measure.
36) List the three main minerals needed for healthy plant growth, and what they're needed for.
37) What are the perils of monoculture?
38) What are auxins? Where are they produced? What happens if you cut a shoot tip off?
39) There are four ways that auxins affect roots and shoots. Give full details for all four.
40) List the four commercial uses for plant hormones. How are seedless grapes made?
41) Explain what rooting compound is used for. How do hormonal weed killers work?

Nutrition

There are *seven* different types of "*nutrients*" which all animals need in their diet.
Make sure you know all about them:

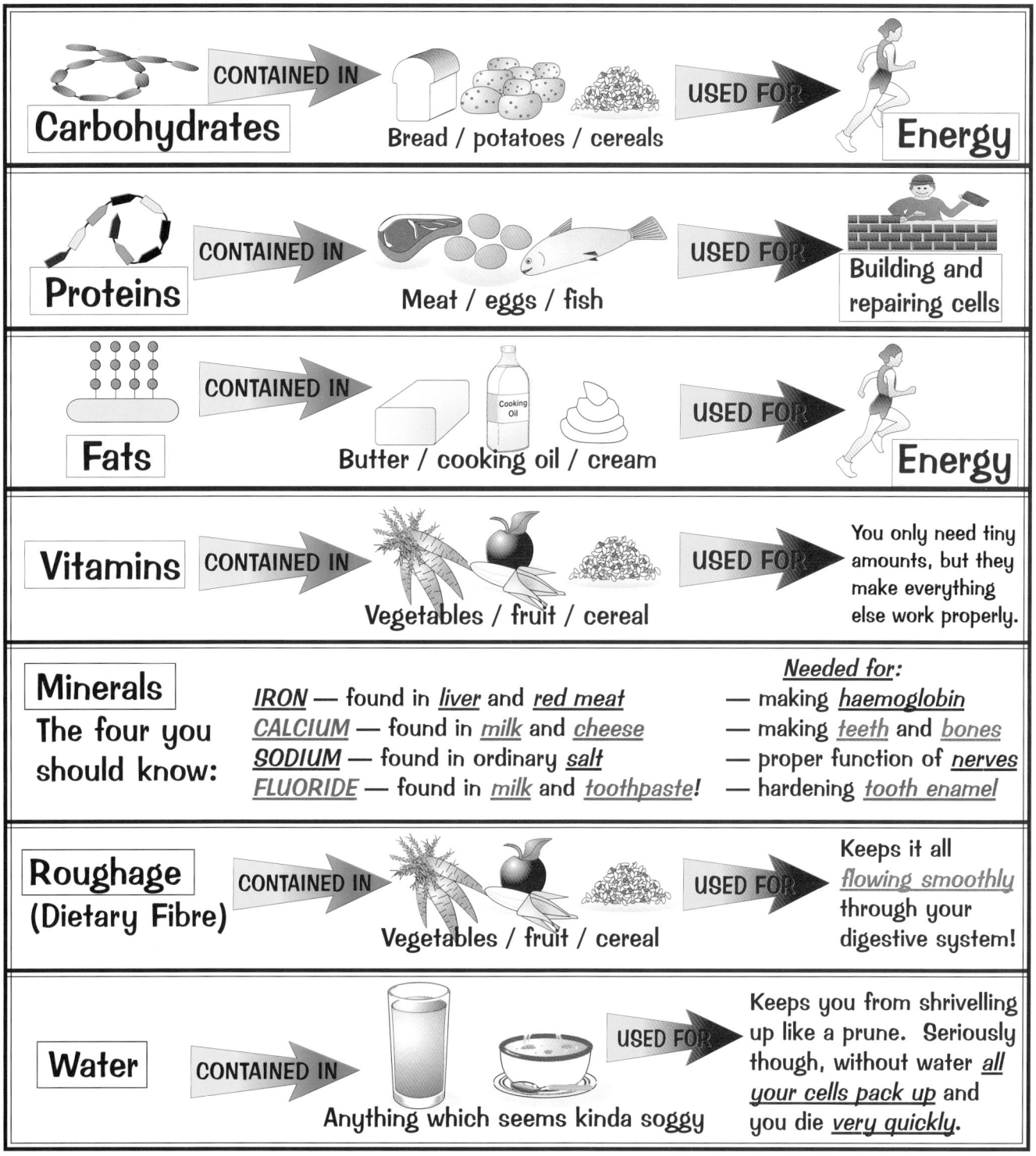

Well there's some food for thought anyway...

There's a fair bit of information on this page and any of it could come up in your Exam.
So sit and learn it. Then turn the page and try and *scribble* it all down again.
And just keep practising till you can answer these two questions without looking back.

1) What are the seven different types of nutrient? What is each one used for in your body?
2) *For each one* name *three* foods which contain them.

The Digestive System

You'll definitely get a question on this in your Exam so take your time and learn this very important diagram in all its infinite glory. And that includes the words too:

Ten Bits of Your Grisly Digestive System to Learn:

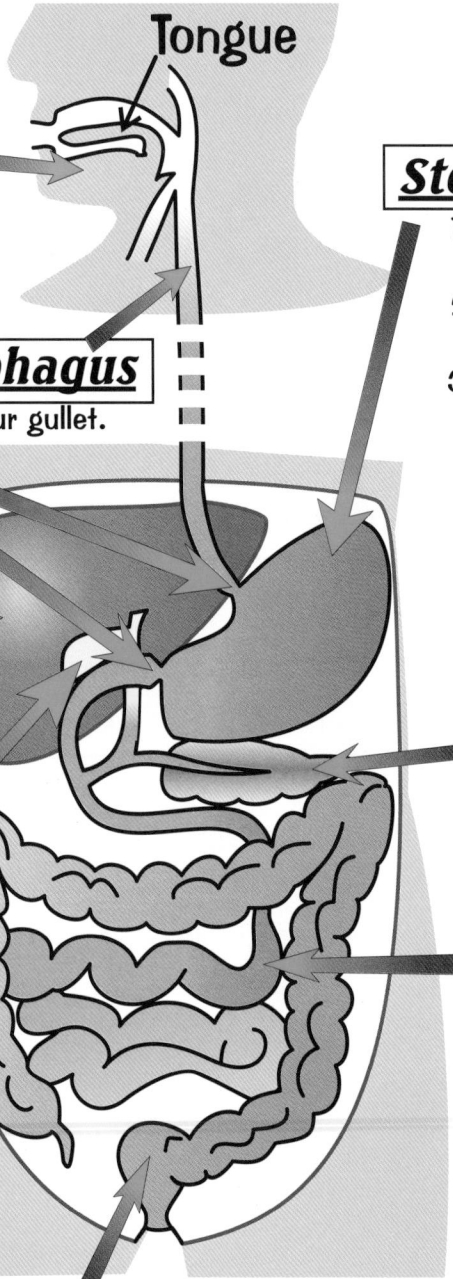

Salivary Glands

These produce a CARBOHYDRASE enzyme called SALIVARY AMYLASE

Oesophagus

Your gullet.

Sphincters

Rings of muscle which are squeezed shut most of the time.

Liver

Gall bladder

Large intestine

Where excess water is absorbed from the food.

Rectum

Where the faeces are stored before they bid you a fond farewell through the anus.

Stomach

1) It PUMMELS THE FOOD with its muscular walls.
2) It produces the PROTEASE enzyme.
3) It produces HYDROCHLORIC ACID for two reasons:
   a) To kill bacteria
   b) To give the right pH for the protease enzyme to work (pH2 — acidic).

Pancreas

Produces all three enzymes: PROTEASE, CARBOHYDRASE and LIPASE.

Small intestine

1) Produces all the three enzymes: PROTEASE, CARBOHYDRASE and LIPASE.
2) This is also where the "food" is absorbed into the blood.
3) The inner surface is covered with villi to increase the surface area. It's also very long.

Have You Learned The Whole Diagram?

The one thing they won't ask you to do in the Exam is draw the whole thing out yourself. But they will ask you about any part of it, e.g. "Which bit is the liver?", or "What does the pancreas produce?", or "What is the job of the small intestine?" So in the end you have to learn the whole thing anyway. And that means being able to cover the page and draw it out, words and all. If you can't draw it all out from memory — then you haven't learnt it. Simple as that.

Digestive Enzymes

There are only THREE MAIN DIGESTIVE ENZYMES. Sadly they all have silly names that can be hard to learn and their "products of digestion" all have suitably silly names too. Ah well — that's Biology for you!

Enzymes break down Big Molecules into Small Ones

1) Starch, proteins and fats are big molecules which can't pass through cell walls into the blood.
2) Sugars, amino acids and fatty acids/glycerol are much smaller molecules which can pass easily into the blood.
3) Enzymes act as catalysts to break down the big molecules into the smaller ones.

1) Carbohydrase Converts Starch into Simple Sugars

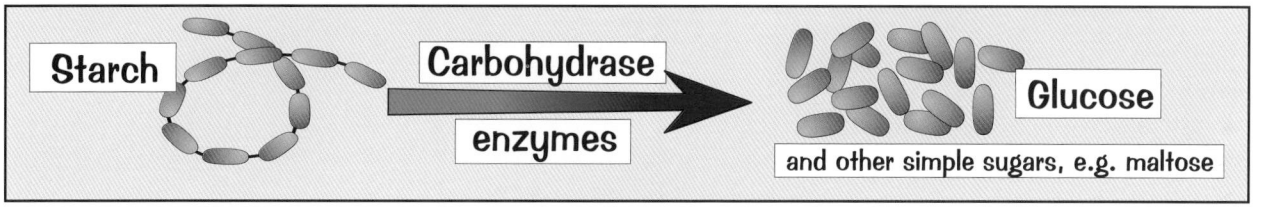

Carbohydrase is produced in three places:
1) THE SALIVARY GLANDS (where it's called "amylase")
2) THE PANCREAS
3) THE SMALL INTESTINE

2) Protease Converts Proteins into Amino Acids

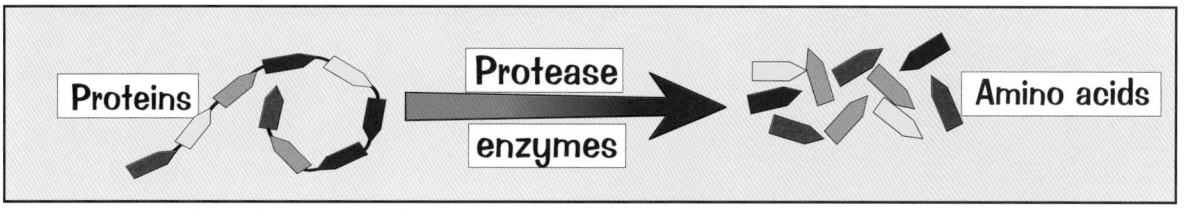

Protease is produced in three places:
1) THE STOMACH (where it's called pepsin)
2) THE PANCREAS
3) THE SMALL INTESTINE

3) Lipase Converts Fats into Fatty Acids and Glycerol

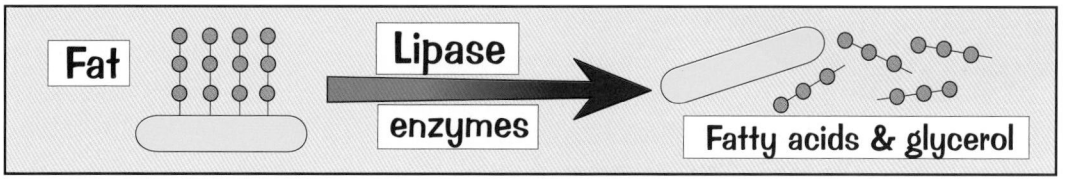

Lipase is produced in two places:
1) THE PANCREAS
2) THE SMALL INTESTINE

Yes, you have to know all that stuff too...

OK it's a pretty dreary page of boring facts, but it all counts — you're expected to know every bit of information on this page. So, take a deep breath, read it and learn it, then cover the page and scribble it all down. Then try again, and again... until you can do it. Fun isn't it.

Teeth

Teeth are Great but they Rot if you don't Clean Them

1) Tooth decay is caused by bacteria which live on your teeth.
2) They feed on sugar and produce acid which dissolves the enamel on your teeth.
3) Fluoride in toothpaste helps strengthen the enamel to resist acid attack.
4) But the only way to keep your teeth from rotting away is to make sure you clean them properly — twice a day. EVERY DAY.
5) If you leave food and bacteria festering away around your gum line, you'll start losing your teeth before you can say "Toothpaste is Ace". Remember: Clean teeth are happy teeth. ☺

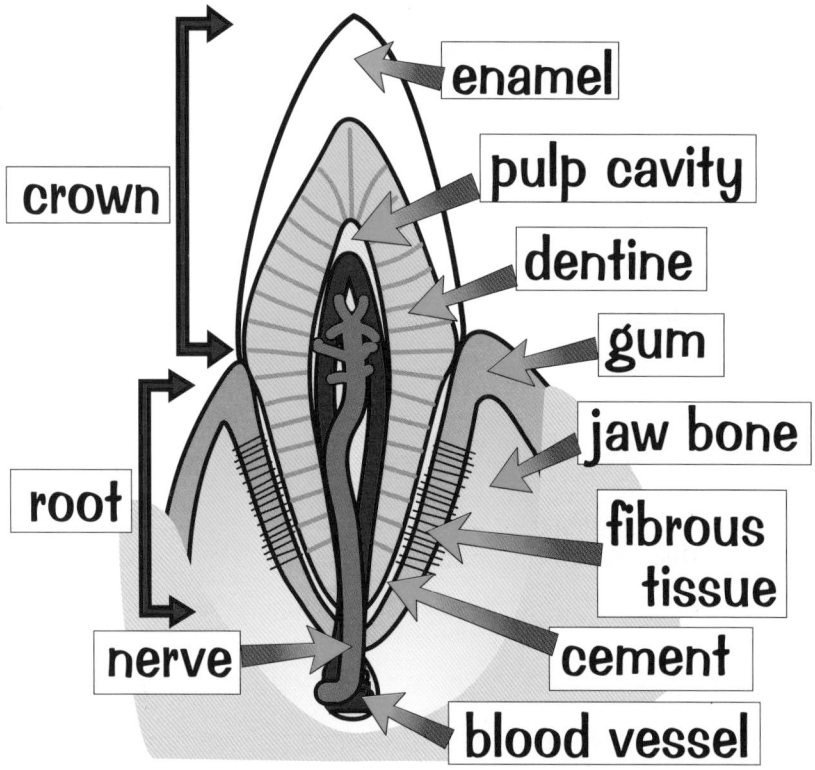

Make sure you know the Four Different Types of Teeth:

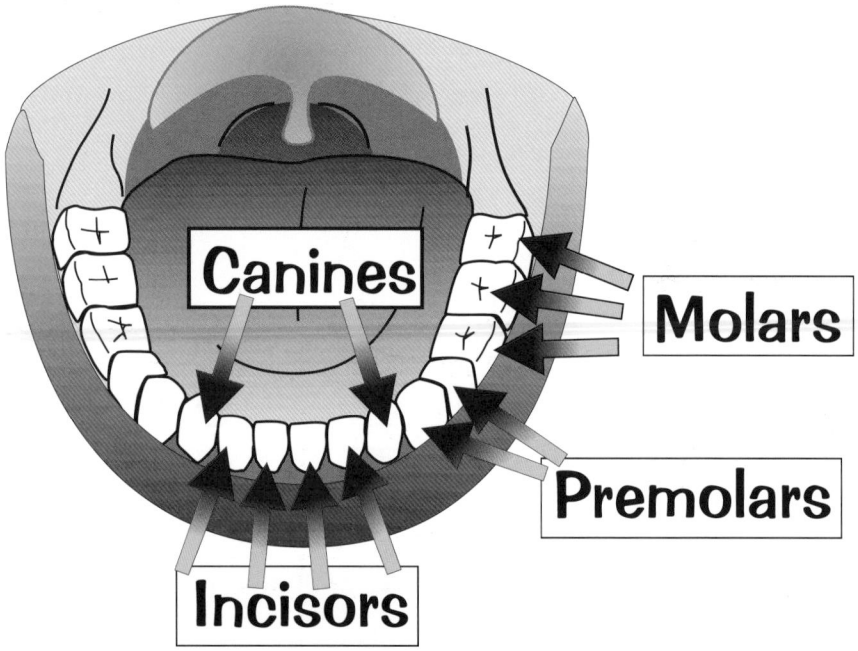

1) INCISORS are for cutting through food.
2) CANINES are used for piercing the prey to get a firm grip on them, and to kill them more quickly.
Canines are much bigger in dogs and cats and other predatory animals.
Humans make little use of them, although a few ruffian sportsmen do have a go from time to time — with some effect, it has to be said.
3) PREMOLARS and MOLARS are for chewing and grinding up food.

More gripping facts to get your teeth into...

A real clever trick for learning lots of information is to get an overall image in your head of what each page looks like. It can really help you to remember all the little details.

1) Try it with this page. Learn the two diagrams, with all their jolly labels.
2) Then cover the page and try and picture the whole thing in your head.
3) Then try and scribble it all down. It takes practise but you can do it.

Muscular and Glandular Tissue

Here are two extra features about the digestive system you should know:

All the Way Along there's Muscular and Glandular Tissue

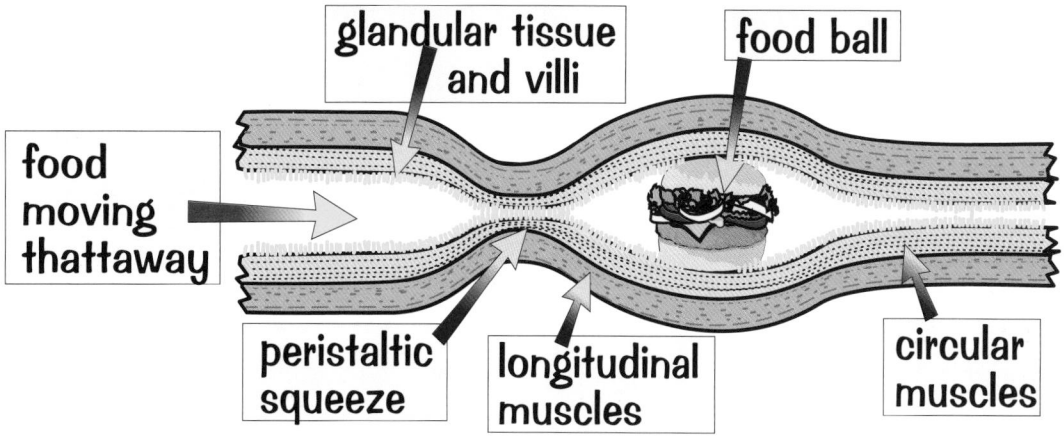

1) There's muscular tissue all the way down the digestive system. Its job is to squeeze the food along. This squeezing action is called PERISTALSIS.

2) The inside layer is glandular tissue which produces the various enzymes, as well as protective mucus.

The Villi Provide a Really Really Big Surface Area

1) The inside of the small intestine is covered in millions and millions of these tiny little things shaped like fingers. They're called VILLI. A single one is called a villus.

2) They increase the surface area in a big way so that digested food is absorbed much more quickly into the blood.

3) Notice they have
   a) a very thin layer of cells
   b) a very good blood supply.

   These two features assist quick absorption.

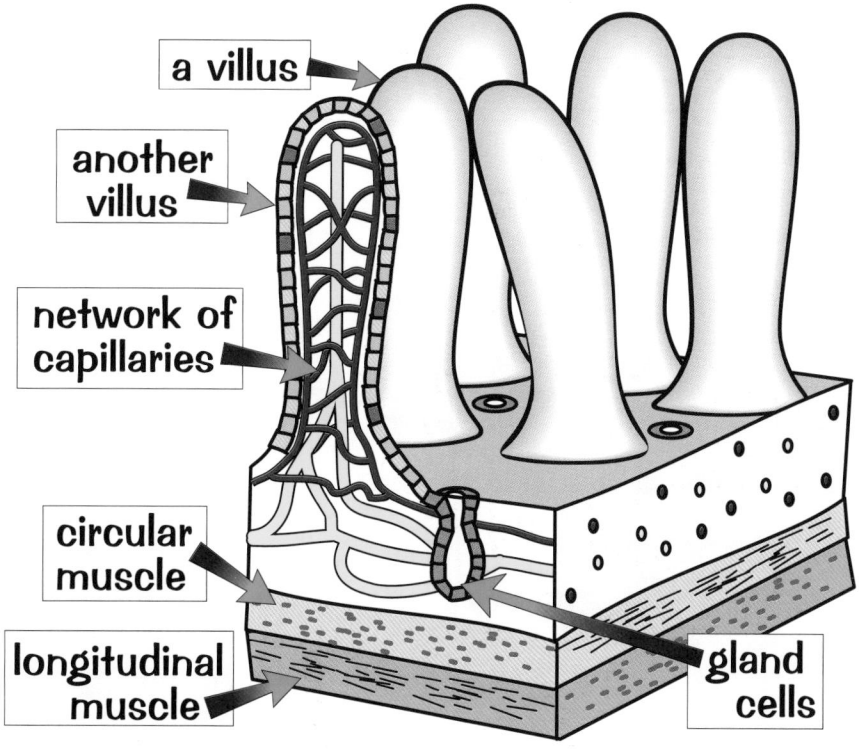

Another absorbing topic for you to learn...

Just like the last page, it can really help if you get a picture in your head of what the whole page looks like, with the two diagrams and the numbered points. Then cover the page and try to scribble the whole thing down again. It does help to know that there are two numbered points for the top section and three for the bottom section. Learn, scribble , check, relearn, scribble...

Diffusion of "Food" Molecules

The Big Food Molecules Must First be Broken Down

After you've *chewed* your food up and then your *stomach's had its turn* at munching it up still further, it's still made up of *quite big molecules*, namely: *STARCH*, *PROTEINS* and *FATS*. These are still *TOO BIG* to diffuse into the blood, and so they are *broken down* in the *small intestine* into *smaller molecules*: *GLUCOSE*, *AMINO ACIDS* and *FATTY ACIDS* & *GLYCEROL*.

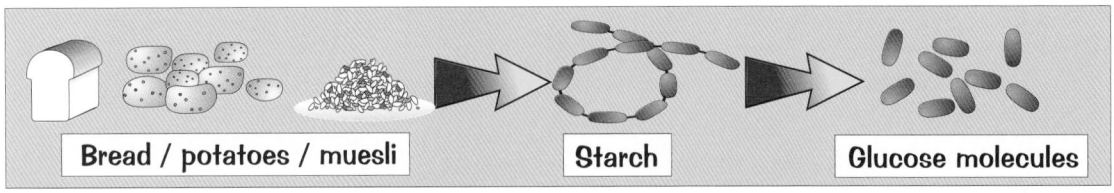

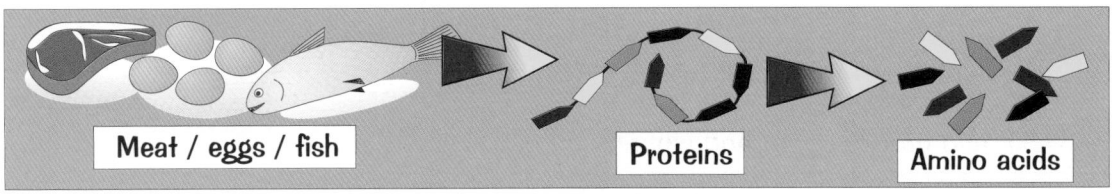

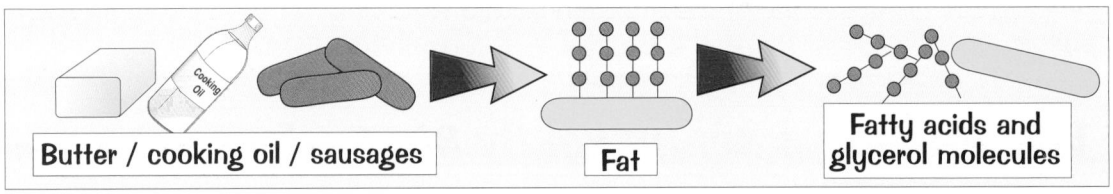

The Small Molecules Can Then Diffuse into the Blood

These molecules (glucose, amino acids, fatty acids and glycerol) are then *small enough* to *diffuse into the blood*.

They then *travel to where they're needed*, and then *diffuse out again*.
It's all clever stuff.

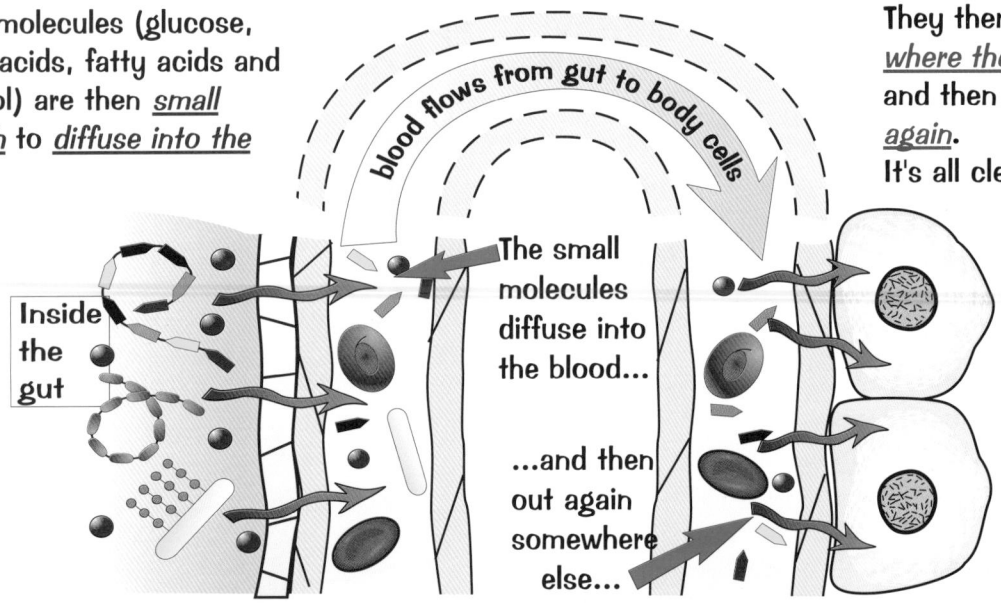

Let's See What You've LEARNED, shall we...

Practise answering these three questions until you can do them all *without looking at the page*. If you can't, then it means just one thing — you haven't learnt it. (Pretty obviously)

1) Name the three big molecules that *won't* diffuse into the blood.
2) Name the three small molecules that *will* diffuse into the blood.
3) What is the name of the process that turns the big molecules into the small molecules?

Nutrient Deficiencies and Food Tests

This is a really boring page.

Lack of Protein Prevents proper Growth and Repair

As well as preventing the body from growing and repairing itself properly, lack of protein also causes a disease called KWASHIORKOR which causes the stomach to become bloated.

Lack of Iron Causes Anaemia

Lack of Iron causes ANAEMIA because the red blood cells don't contain enough haemoglobin, which is made from iron. This makes the person look pale. They also feel tired because their blood can't carry enough oxygen to their cells.

Lack of Calcium Causes Brittle Bones and Teeth

Lack of Calcium causes BRITTLE BONES AND TEETH and poor growth of bones and teeth in kids.

Lack of Vitamin C Causes Skin Problems like Scurvy

Lack of vitamin C causes SCURVY AND OTHER SKIN DISORDERS. Without vitamin C the skin becomes weak and cracks open, and wounds do not heal.

Lack of Vitamin D Causes Bones to Stay Soft — Rickets

Not enough vitamin D causes the BONES TO STAY SOFT and they bend.
This is known as RICKETS and it usually shows up as "bow legs" which happens if a child grows up without enough vitamin D.

Four Seriously boring Food Tests

1) The Iodine Test for STARCH — turns it Blue/black

1) Add some drops of brown iodine solution to the food.
2) If it contains STARCH the iodine will turn blue/black.

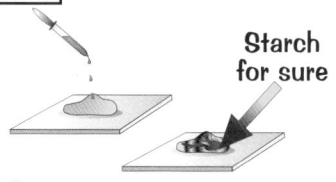

2) The Biuret test for PROTEIN — turns $CuSO_4$ Purple

1) First add some sodium hydroxide (NaOH) solution and shake with care.
2) Then add some weak copper sulphate solution.
3) If the pale blue colour turns purple there's PROTEIN present.

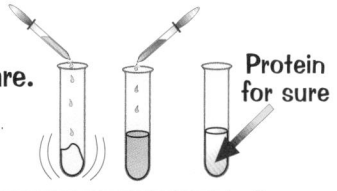

3) The Benedict's test for SIMPLE SUGARS — an Orange Precipitate

1) Add blue BENEDICT'S SOLUTION to the food in a test tube. Bring to the boil.
2) If you get an orange precipitate then the food contains SIMPLE SUGARS.

4) The Alcohol-Emulsion test for FATS

1) Mix the food with pure ethanol and then filter it.
2) Add the clear solution to water.
3) A white emulsion indicates the food contains FATS.

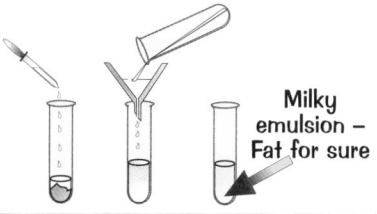

Got any Deficiencies? — Test Yourself Here...

What a grim-looking page this is. No decent diagrams, just lots of boring facts.
Trouble is you've still gotta learn it. Toughsky. You know the drill though: cover the page, then scribble it down from memory until you remember all the facts without having to look back.
Remember, this book isn't full of drivel. Just all the basic facts which YOU have to learn.

The Circulatory System

The circulatory system's main function is to get food and oxygen to every cell in the body. The diagram shows the basic layout, but make sure you learn the five important points too.

The DOUBLE Circulatory System, actually

① The *HEART* is actually *TWO PUMPS*. The *RIGHT SIDE* pumps deoxygenated blood to the *LUNGS* to *COLLECT OXYGEN*. Then the *LEFT SIDE* pumps this oxygenated blood *AROUND THE BODY*.

② *ARTERIES* carry blood *away from the heart* at *HIGH PRESSURE*.

③ Normally, arteries carry *OXYGENATED BLOOD* and veins carry *DEOXYGENATED BLOOD*.

The *pulmonary artery* and *pulmonary vein* are the *big exceptions* to this rule (see diagram).

④ The arteries eventually *SPLIT OFF* into *thousands of tiny capillaries* which take blood to *every cell in the body*.

⑤ The *VEINS* then collect the *"used" blood* and carry it *back to the heart* at *low pressure* to be pumped round again.

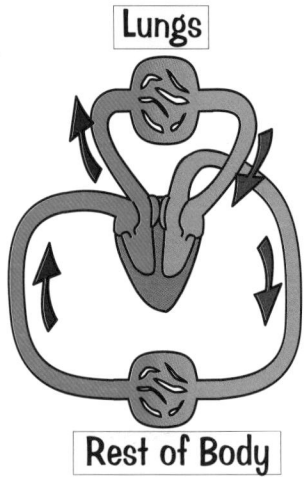

brain
jugular vein
carotid artery
superior vena cava
aorta
lungs
pulmonary vein
pulmonary artery
dorsal aorta
heart
hepatic artery
hepatic vein
hepatic portal vein
liver
gut
inferior vena cava
kidneys
renal artery
renal vein
from lower limbs
to lower limbs

Fish don't have a double circulation system, but all fast-moving creatures like mammals and birds do. If you think about it, it's a mighty clever system to have evolved all by itself. Goodness knows how it ever happened.
I mean how could a single pump system "evolve" into a double one like this? It's got to be all or nothing for it to work hasn't it? That's quite a mutation, to go straight from a single pump heart that pumps to the lungs and then on to the rest of the body, to the double pump system shown above. But then life's full of little mysteries isn't it!

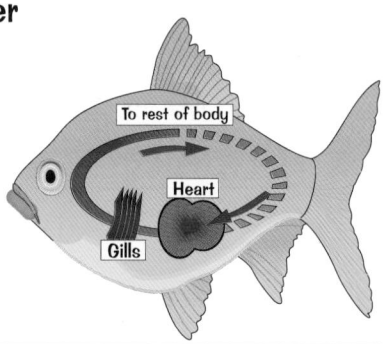

Let's See What You Know then...

At least this stuff on the circulatory system is fairly interesting. Mind you, there are still plenty of picky little details you need to be clear about. And yes, you've guessed it, there's one surefire way to check just how clear you are — *read it, learn it, then cover the page and reproduce it*.
Having to sketch the diagram out again *from memory* is the only way to *really learn it*.

The Heart

The heart is made almost entirely of *muscle*. And it's a *double pump*. Visualise this diagram with its *bigger side* full of *red, oxygenated blood*, and its *smaller side* full of *blue, deoxygenated blood*, and learn that the *left side* is *bigger*.

Learn This Diagram of the Heart with All its Labels

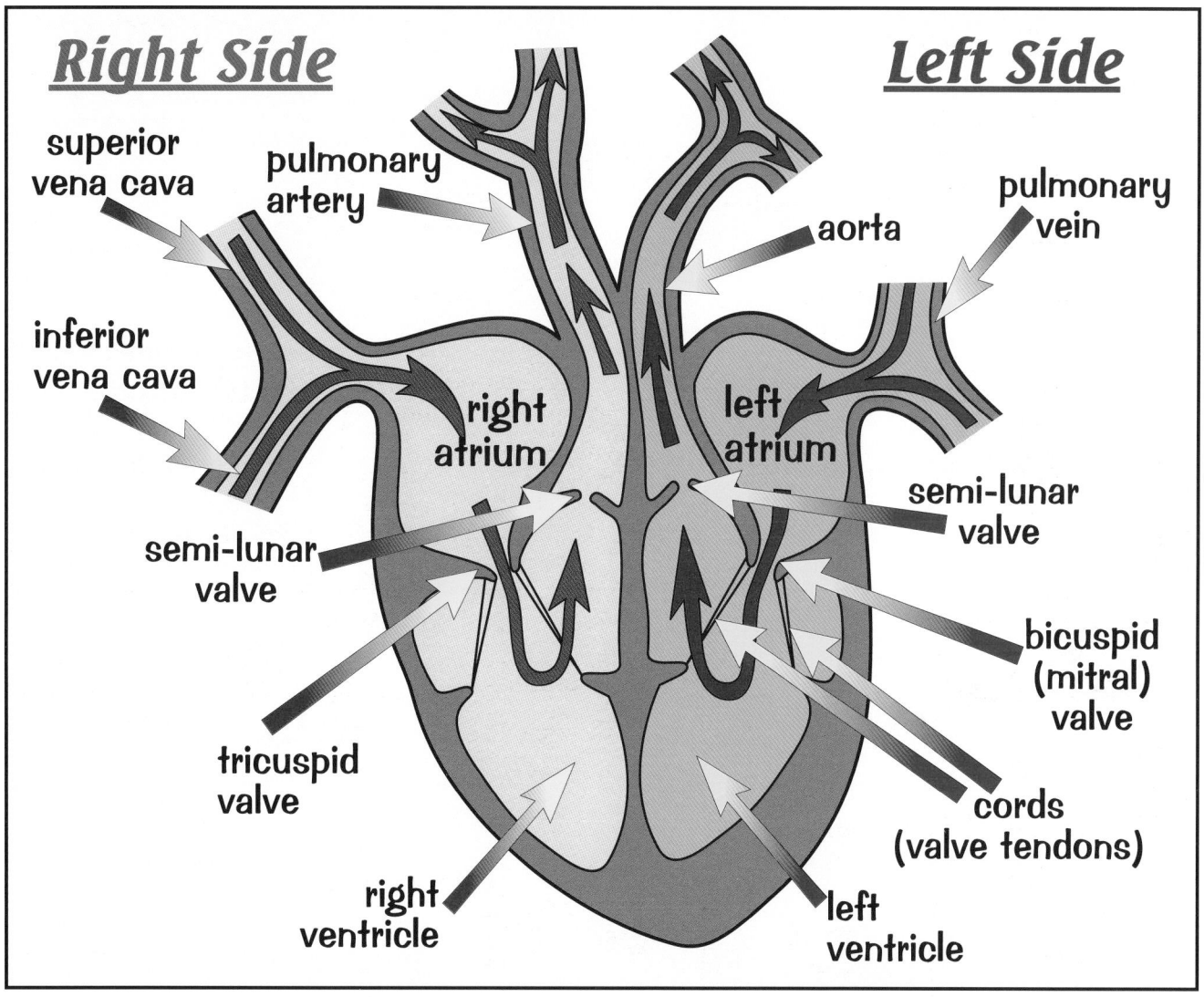

Four Extra Details to Delight and Thrill You

1) The *right side* of the heart receives *deoxygenated blood* from the body and *pumps it only to the lungs*, so it has *thinner walls* than the left side.

2) The *left side* receives *oxygenated blood* from the lungs and *pumps it out round the whole body*, so it has *thicker, more muscular walls*.

3) The *ventricles* are *much bigger* than the *atria* because they push blood *round the body*.

4) The *valves* are for *preventing backflow* of blood.

OK Let's get to the Heart of the Matter...

They quite often put a diagram of the heart in the Exam and ask you to label parts of it. There's only one way to be sure you can label it all and that's to learn the diagram until you can sketch it out, with all the labels, *from memory*. Also *learn* the four points at the bottom.

The Pumping Cycle

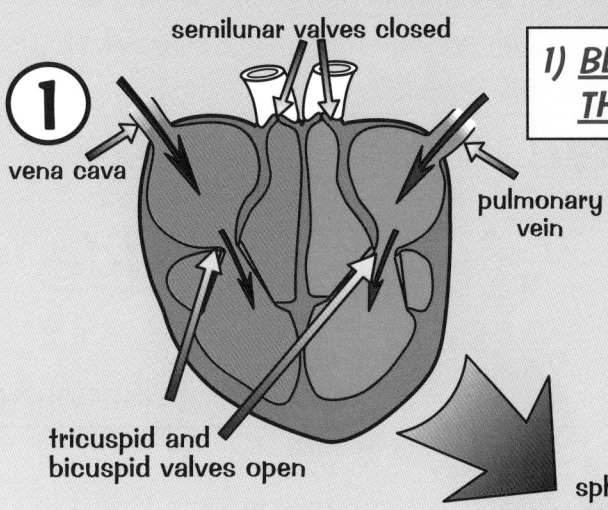

1) BLOOD FLOWS INTO THE TWO ATRIA.

Learn the Three Stages of The Pumping Cycle

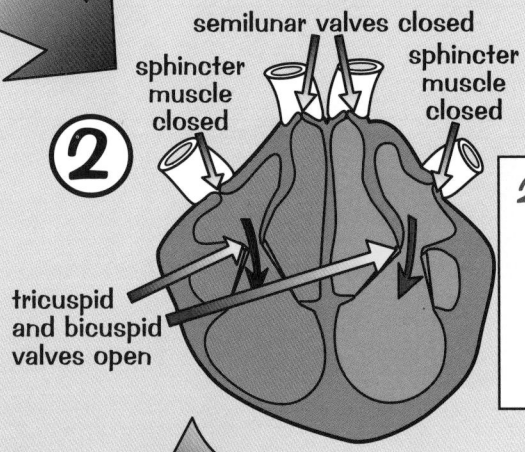

2) THE ATRIA GIVE A GENTLE BEAT to push the blood into the VENTRICLES.

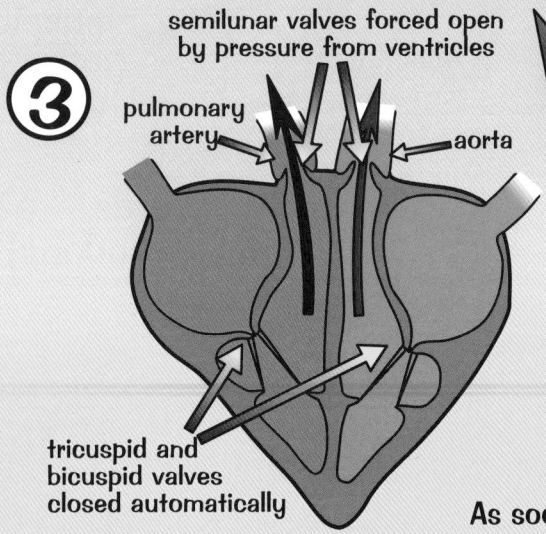

3) THE VENTRICLES CONTRACT forcing blood into the AORTA and PULMONARY ARTERY.

The *VENTRICLES* are much more *POWERFUL*, and when they beat the *bicuspid and tricuspid valves* pop shut automatically *to prevent backflow* into the atria. Sphincters wouldn't be strong enough.

As soon as the ventricles relax, *the semilunar valves pop shut* to prevent backflow of blood (back into the ventricles) as it is now under *a fair bit of pressure* in the arteries.

4) THE BLOOD FLOWS DOWN THE ARTERIES, THE ATRIA FILL AGAIN AND THE WHOLE CYCLE STARTS OVER.

If this doesn't get your pulse racing, nothing will...

You need to know the details of each step of the pumping cycle. They will quite cheerfully give you a diagram similar to one of the above and ask you which valves are open or where the blood is flowing, etc. etc. Make sure you can *sketch out* all three diagrams *from memory*.

Blood Vessels

There are three different types of blood vessel and you need to know all about them:

Arteries Carry Blood Under Pressure

1) ARTERIES carry oxygenated blood away from the heart.
2) It comes out of the heart at HIGH PRESSURE, so the artery walls have to be STRONG AND ELASTIC.
3) Note how THICK the walls are compared to the size of the hole down the middle (the "lumen" — silly name!)

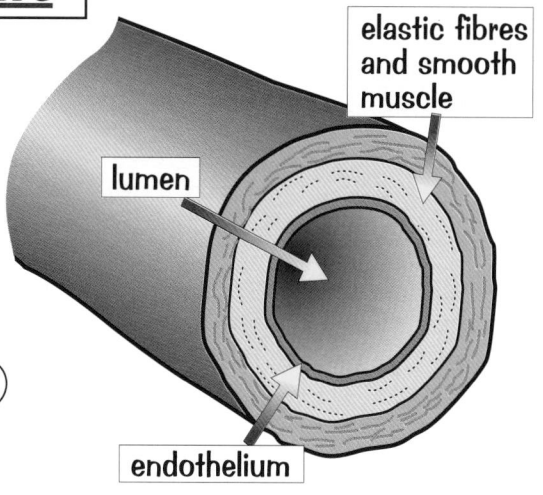

Capillaries are Real Small

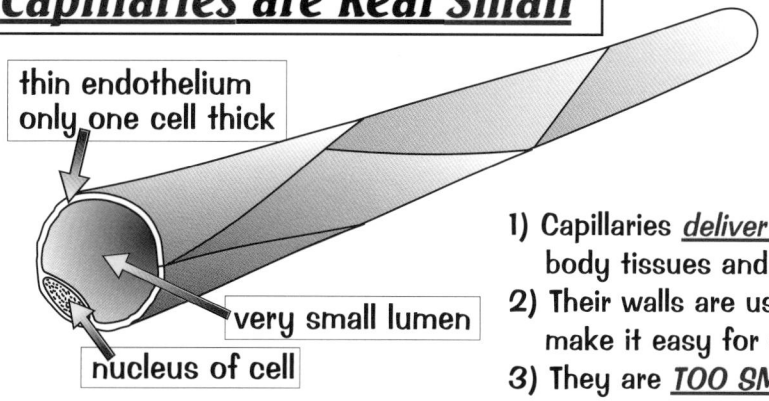

1) Capillaries deliver food and oxygen direct to the body tissues and take waste products away.
2) Their walls are usually ONLY ONE CELL THICK to make it easy for stuff to pass in and out of them.
3) They are TOO SMALL to see.

Veins Take Blood Back to The Heart

1) VEINS carry DEOXYGENATED BLOOD back to the heart.
2) The blood is at LOWER PRESSURE in the veins so the walls do not need to be so thick.
3) They have a BIGGER LUMEN than arteries TO HELP BLOOD FLOW.
4) They also have VALVES to help keep the blood flowing IN THE RIGHT DIRECTION.

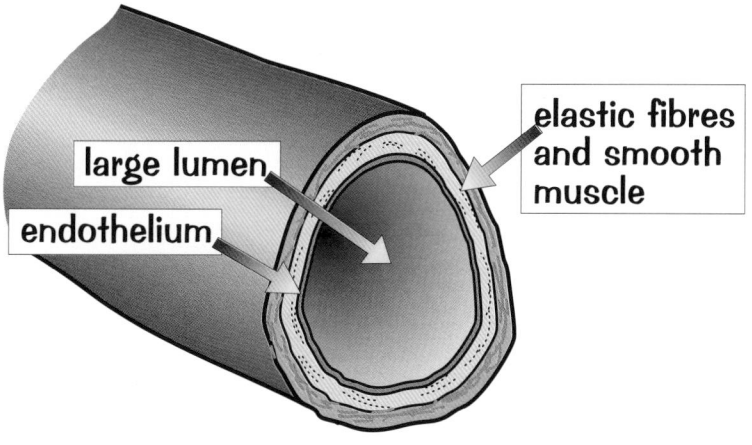

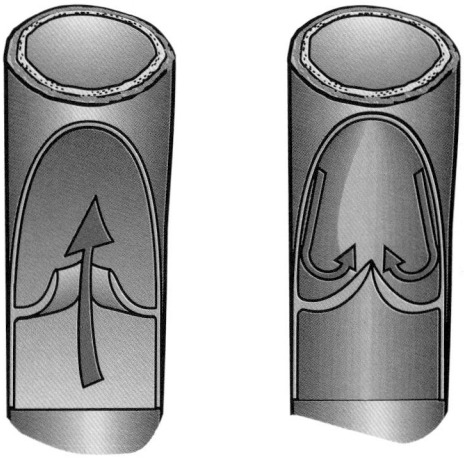

Don't Struggle in Vain...

Let's face it these are mighty easy diagrams to learn. Just make sure you learn the numbered points as well. I reckon it can't take more than two or three attempts before you can scribble out the whole of this page, diagrams and all, entirely from memory. Concentrate on learning the bits you forgot each time, of course. Try it and see how right I am!

Blood

Red Blood Cells

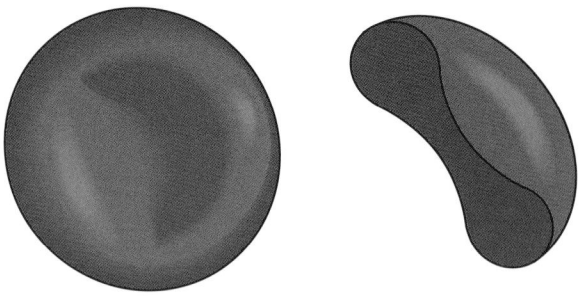

1) Their job is to CARRY OXYGEN to all the cells in the body.
2) They have a FLYING DOUGHNUT SHAPE to give MAXIMUM SURFACE AREA for absorbing oxygen.
3) They contain HAEMOGLOBIN which is very RED, and which contains a lot of IRON.
4) In the lungs, haemoglobin absorbs oxygen to become OXYHAEMOGLOBIN. In body tissues the reverse happens to release oxygen to the cells.
5) Red blood cells have NO NUCLEUS to make more room for haemoglobin.

White Blood Cells

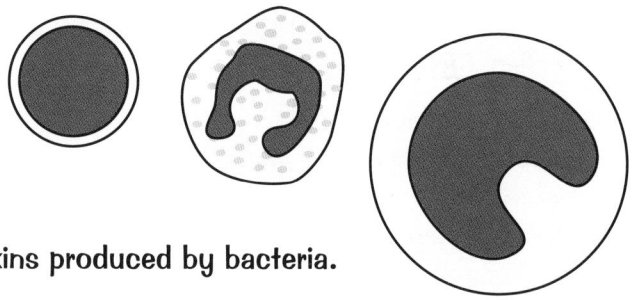

1) Their main role is DEFENCE AGAINST DISEASE.
2) They have a BIG NUCLEUS.
3) They GOBBLE UP UNWELCOME MICROBES.
4) They produce ANTIBODIES to fight bacteria.
5) They produce ANTITOXINS to neutralise the toxins produced by bacteria.

Plasma

This is a pale straw-coloured liquid which CARRIES JUST ABOUT EVERYTHING:

1) RED and WHITE BLOOD CELLS and PLATELETS.
2) Digested food products like GLUCOSE and AMINO ACIDS.
3) CARBON DIOXIDE.
4) UREA.
5) HORMONES.
6) ANTIBODIES and ANTITOXINS produced by the white blood cells.

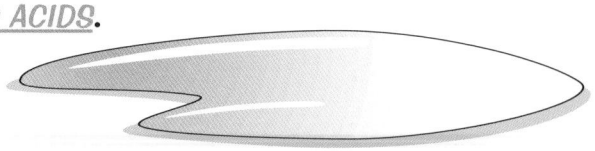

Platelets

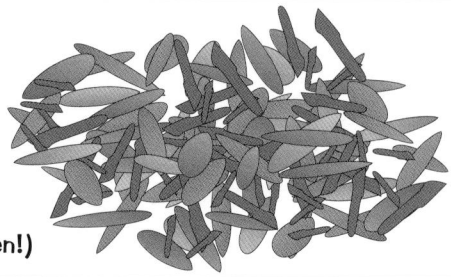

1) These are SMALL FRAGMENTS OF CELLS.
2) They have NO NUCLEUS.
3) They HELP THE BLOOD TO CLOT at a wound.

(So basically they just float about waiting for accidents to happen!)

More Blood, Sweat and Tears...

Do the same as usual — learn the facts until you can write them down from memory.

Just in case you think all this formal learning is a waste of time, how do you think you'd get on with these typical Exam questions if you didn't learn it all first?

THREE TYPICAL EXAM QUESTIONS:

1) What is the function of blood plasma? (4 marks)
2) What do white blood cells do? (3 marks)
3) What is the function of haemoglobin? (4 marks)

Lungs and Breathing

The Thorax

Learn this diagram real good.

1) The ***THORAX*** is the top part of your "body".
2) The ***LUNGS*** are like ***BIG PINK SPONGES***.
3) The ***TRACHEA*** splits into two tubes called "***BRONCHI***" (each one is "a bronchus"), one going to each lung.
4) The bronchi split into progressively smaller tubes called ***BRONCHIOLES***.
5) The bronchioles finally end at small bags called ***ALVEOLI*** where the gas exchange takes place.

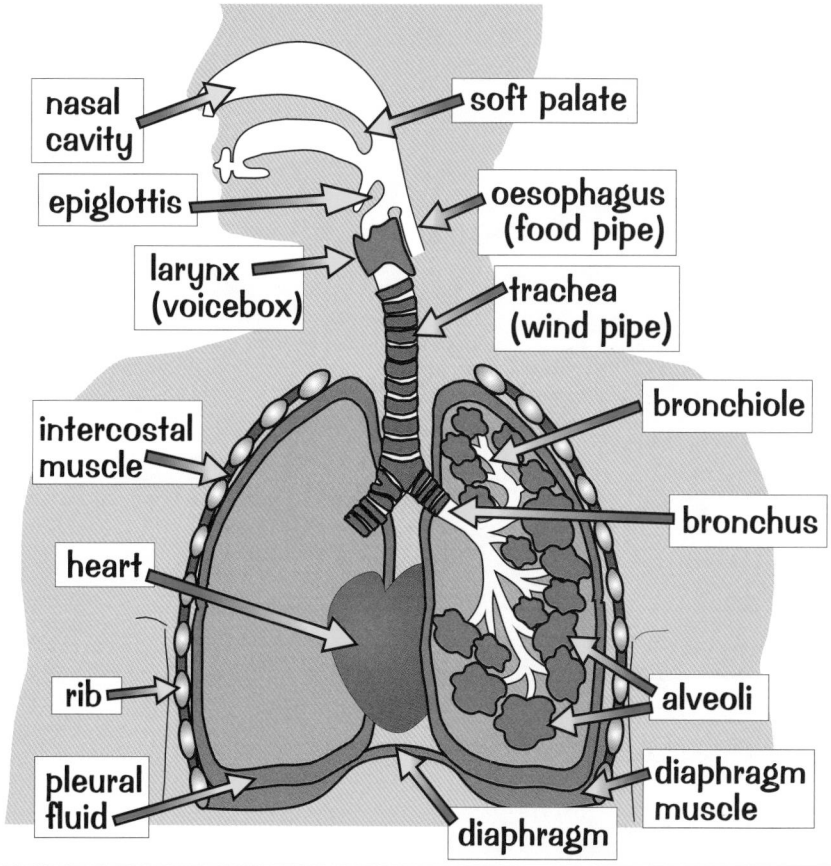

Breathing In...

1) *Intercostals* and *diaphragm* ***CONTRACT***.
2) *Thorax volume* ***INCREASES***.
3) Air is ***DRAWN IN***.

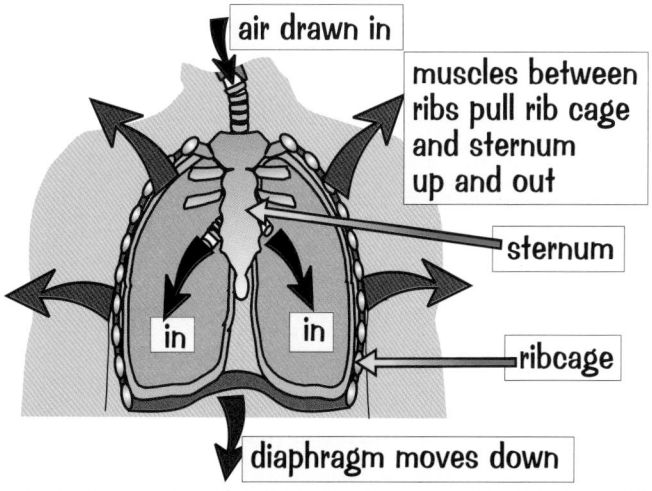

...and Breathing Out

1) *Intercostals* and *diaphragm* ***RELAX***.
2) *Thorax volume* ***DECREASES***.
3) Air is ***FORCED OUT***.

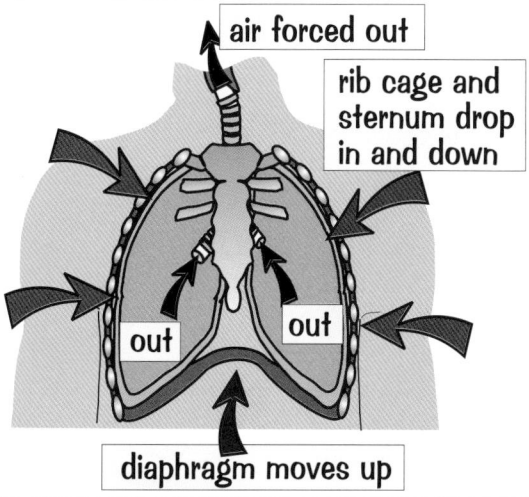

Stop Huffing and Puffing and just LEARN IT...

No dreary lists of facts this time anyway, just three splendid diagrams to learn.
When you practise repeating diagrams from memory, you don't have to draw them really neatly, just sketch them clear enough to label all the important bits. They would never ask you to draw a really fancy diagram in the Exam, but they will expect you to label one. But the only way to be sure you really know a diagram is to sketch it and label it, *all from memory*.

Alveoli, Cells and Diffusion

Alveoli

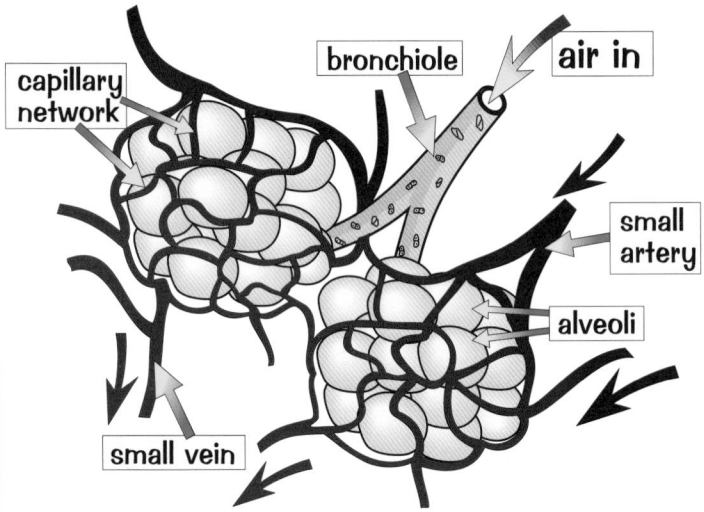

The *ALVEOLI* are an ideal *EXCHANGE SURFACE*. They have:

1) An *ENORMOUS SURFACE AREA* (about $70m^2$ in total).
2) A *MOIST LINING* for dissolving gases.
3) Very *THIN WALLS*.
4) A *COPIOUS BLOOD SUPPLY*.

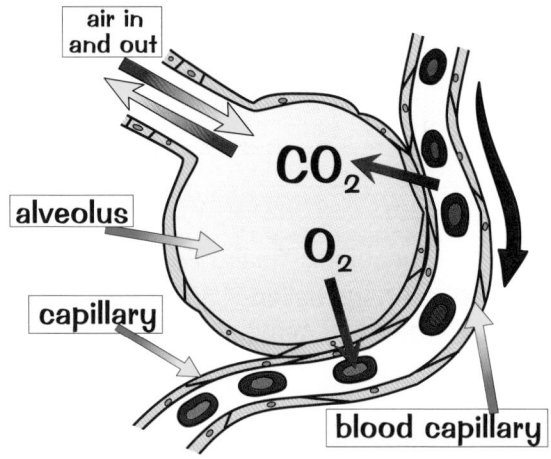

1) The job of the lungs is to *transfer OXYGEN to the blood* and to *remove waste CARBON DIOXIDE* from it.

2) To do this *the lungs contain millions of ALVEOLI* where *GAS EXCHANGE* takes place.

Gas Exchange at the Cells

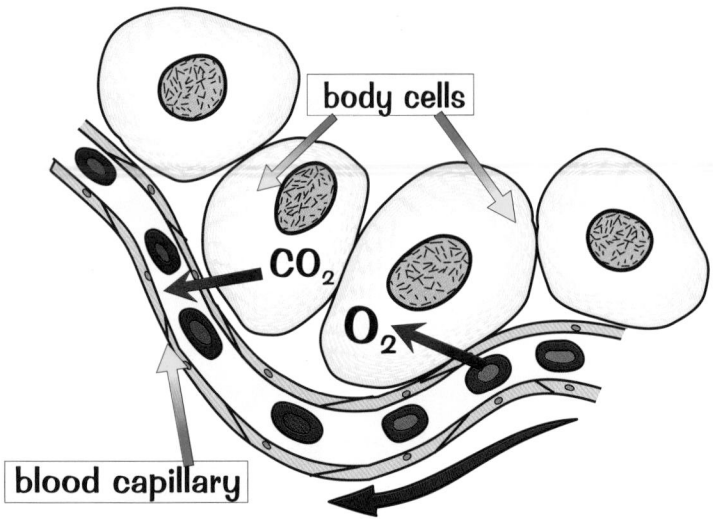

1) When the blood reaches the *CELLS*, *OXYGEN IS RELEASED* from the *OXYHAEMOGLOBIN* in the red blood cells *AND DIFFUSES INTO THE BODY CELLS*.

2) At the same time, *CARBON DIOXIDE DIFFUSES INTO THE BLOOD* (plasma) to be carried back to the lungs.

This is a very Easy Page To Learn...

Notice that the numbered points repeat information that the diagrams already show very clearly. The big idea is that you should *understand and remember* what goes on and why it all works so well. A clear visual image in your head of these diagrams makes it a lot easier. *Learn* the diagrams, words and all, until you can sketch them out *entirely from memory*.

Respiration

Respiration is NOT "breathing in and out"

1) Respiration is NOT breathing in and breathing out, as you might think.
2) Respiration actually goes on in every cell in your body.
3) Respiration is the process of converting glucose to energy.
4) It takes place in plants too. All living things "respire". They convert "food" into energy.

RESPIRATION is the process of CONVERTING GLUCOSE TO ENERGY, which goes on IN EVERY CELL

Aerobic Respiration Needs Plenty of Oxygen

1) Aerobic respiration is what happens if there's plenty of oxygen available.
2) "Aerobic" just means "with air" and it's the ideal way to convert glucose into energy.

You need to learn THE EQUATION:

Glucose + Oxygen → Carbon Dioxide + Water (+ Energy)

Composition of Inhaled and Exhaled Air

This is the difference between what you BREATHE IN and what you BREATHE OUT:

GAS:	AIR IN:	AIR OUT:
Nitrogen	79%	79%
Oxygen	21%	16%
CO_2	0.04%	4%
Water vapour	Varies	Loads

1) Note that the amount of OXYGEN USED matches the amount of CO_2 PRODUCED, as in the above equation.
2) Notice that even with millions of alveoli, you still only absorb A SMALL PROPORTION OF THE OXYGEN in each breath.

One Big Deep Breath and LEARN IT...

There are three sections on this page and learning them well enough to scribble them down from memory isn't so difficult. Try to visualise the basic page layout and remember how many numbered points there are for each bit. You don't have to write it out word for word, just make sure you remember the important points about each bit.

Anaerobic Respiration — You and Yeast

Anaerobic Respiration doesn't use Oxygen at all

1) *Anaerobic respiration* is what happens if there's *no oxygen available*.
2) "Anaerobic" just means "without air" and it's *NOT the best way to convert glucose into energy*.

You need to learn *THE WORD EQUATION*:

Glucose → Energy + Lactic Acid

3) *Anaerobic respiration* does *not produce nearly as much energy* as aerobic respiration — but it's useful in emergencies.

Fitness and the Oxygen Debt

1) When you do *vigorous exercise* and your *body can't supply enough oxygen* to your muscles they start doing *anaerobic respiration* instead.
2) *This isn't great* because *lactic acid builds up* in the muscles, which gets *painful*.
3) The advantage is that *at least you can keep on using your muscles* for a while longer.
4) After resorting to anaerobic respiration, when you stop you'll have an *oxygen debt*.
5) In other words *you have to "repay" the oxygen* which you didn't manage to get to your muscles in time, because *your lungs, heart and blood couldn't keep up with the demand earlier on*.
6) This means you have to *keep breathing hard for a while after you stop* to get oxygen into your muscles to convert the painful lactic acid to harmless CO_2 and water.
7) When *high levels of CO_2 and lactic acid* are detected in the blood (by the brain), the *pulse and breathing rate are both increased automatically* to try and rectify the situation.
8) *A good measure of fitness* is *how quickly you can recover* to normal breathing and pulse after doing some vigorous exercise. This is called your *recovery time*.

Anaerobic Respiration in Yeast Makes Bread and Beer

YEAST is used for *MAKING BREAD* and for *BREWING BEER*, and in both cases the yeast does the business by performing *ANAEROBIC RESPIRATION*.
Another word for this process is *FERMENTATION*. Learn this formula for it:

Glucose → Alcohol + Carbon Dioxide (+ Energy)

In bread-making as the yeast gets to work *it's the CO_2 which makes the bread rise*.
In brewing, of course *the alcohol's the most important bit*, but the CO_2 also makes it kinda fizzy.
(See the Chemistry Book for more details on fermentation.)

Let's See What you Know Then...

Read the page then see what you can *scribble down* about each of the three sections. *Then try again*. You don't want to try and learn those eight points about "Oxygen Debt" too formally. It's much better to write your own mini-essay on it and then see what stuff you missed. Enjoy.

The Nervous System

Sense Organs and Receptors

THE FIVE SENSE ORGANS ARE:
Eyes ears nose tongue skin

These five different *sense organs* all contain different *receptors*.

Receptors are groups of cells which are *sensitive to a stimulus* such as light or heat, etc.

SENSE ORGANS and **RECEPTORS**
Don't get them mixed up:

The *EYE* is a *SENSE ORGAN* — it contains *LIGHT RECEPTORS*.

The *EAR* is a *SENSE ORGAN* — it contains *SOUND RECEPTORS*.

The *FIVE SENSE ORGANS* and the *stimuli* that each one is *sensitive to*:

1) EYES
Light receptors.

2) EARS
Sound and "*balance*" receptors.

3) NOSE
Taste and *smell* receptors (Chemical stimuli).

4) TONGUE
Taste receptors: Bitter, salt, sweet and sour (Chemical stimuli).

5) SKIN
Touch, *pressure* and *temperature* receptors.

THE CENTRAL NERVOUS SYSTEM
Consists of the *brain* and *spinal cord* only.

MOTOR NEURONES
The *nerve fibres* that carry signals to the *effector* muscle or gland.

SENSORY NEURONES
The *nerve fibres* that carry signals from the *receptors* in the sense organs to the *central nervous system*.

EFFECTORS
All your *muscles* and *glands* will respond to nervous impulses...

This stuff is easy — I mean it's all just common senses...

There's quite a few names to learn here (as ever!).
But there's no drivel. It's all worth marks in the Exam, so learn it all.
Practise until you can *cover the page* and *scribble down* all the details *from memory*.

The Central Nervous System

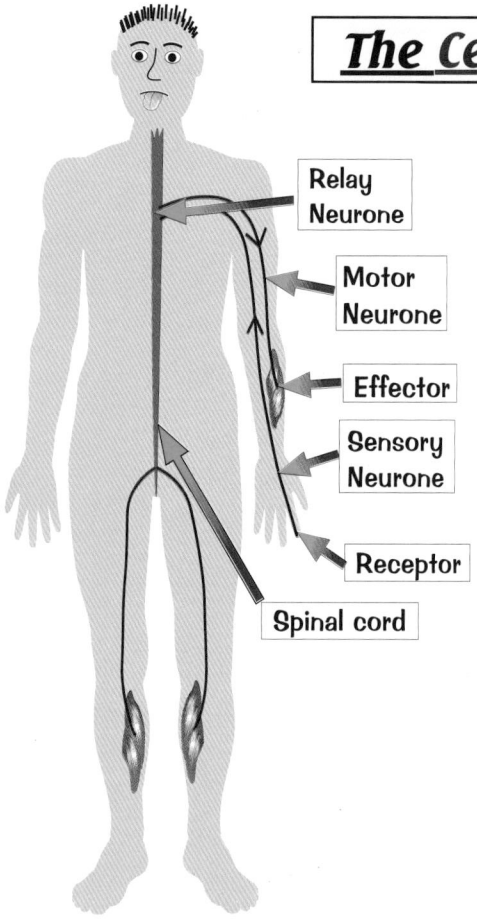

The Central Nervous System and Effectors

1) *THE CENTRAL NERVOUS SYSTEM* is where all the sensory information is sent and where reflexes and actions are coordinated. It consists of *THE BRAIN* and *SPINAL CORD* only.
2) *NEURONES* (nerve cells) *transmit electrical impulses* very quickly around the body.
3) The *EFFECTORS* are *muscles and glands* which respond to the various stimuli according to the instructions sent from the central nervous system.

The Three Types of Neurone are All Pretty Much The Same

The THREE TYPES of NEURONE are:

1) *SENSORY neurone*,
2) *MOTOR neurone*,
3) *RELAY neurone* (or *CONNECTOR neurone*).

They're all *pretty much the same*, but they're *connected to different things*, that's all.

A Typical Neurone:

— *Learn the names* of all the bits:

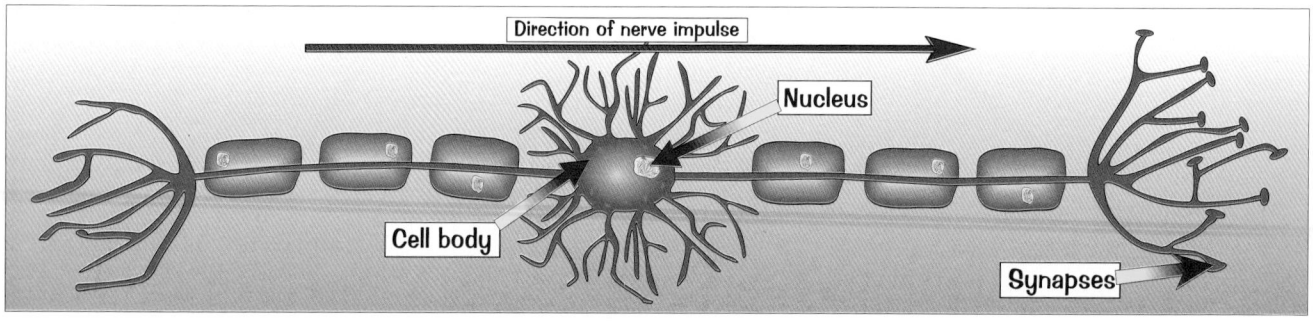

Synapses are the Connections between Nerve fibres

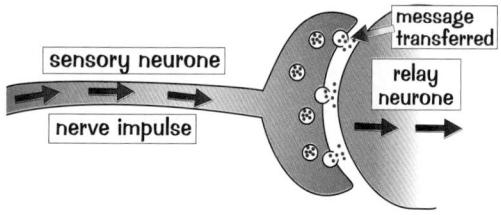

1) The *connection* between *two neurones* is called a *synapse*.
2) The nerve signal is transferred across the gap.
3) This sets off a *new electrical signal* in the *next* neurone.

Don't get all twitchy — just learn it...

Another jolly page to learn, but it's all good clean fun. Once again, everything on this page is important information that you definitely need to know for the Exams. Use the diagrams to help you remember the important details. Then *cover the page* and *scribble it all down*.

Neurones and Reflexes

The Reflex Arc Allows Very Quick Responses

1) The nervous system allows *very quick responses* because it uses *electrical impulses*.

2) *Reflex actions* are ones that you do *without thinking* so they are *even quicker*.

3) Reflex actions *save your body from injury*, e.g. pulling your hand off a hot object for you.

A ***REFLEX ARC*** is simple enough.

It's called an "arc" rather than a loop because the two ends don't connect.

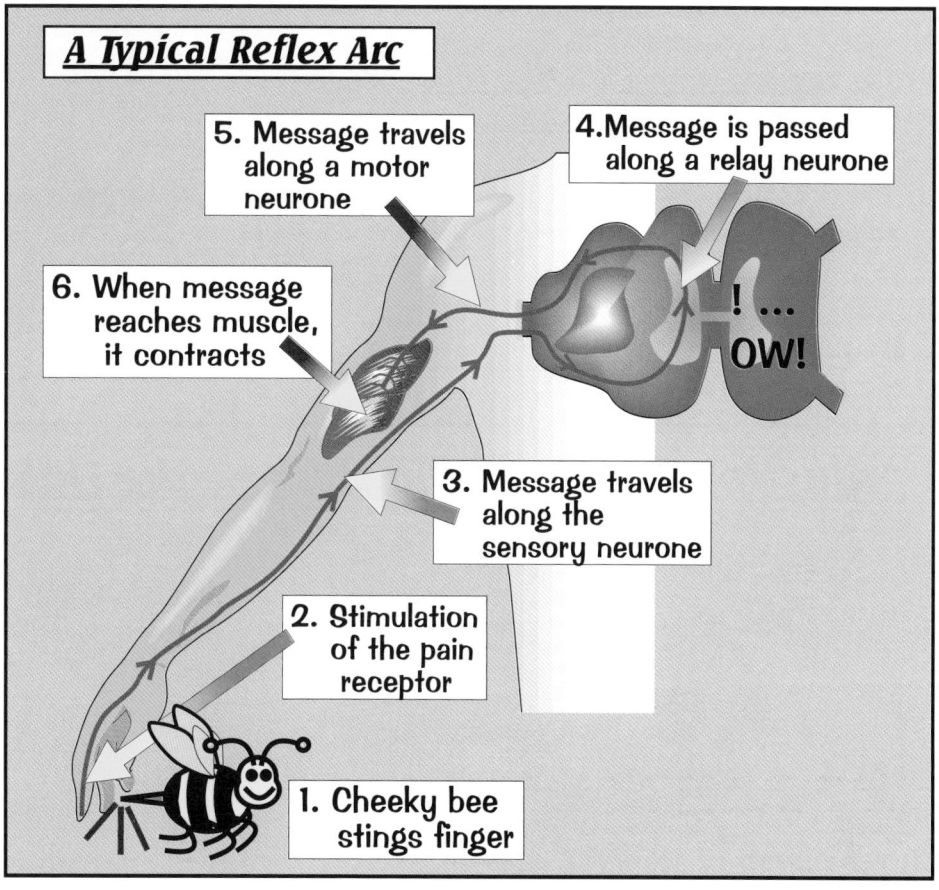

Learn the Block Diagram of A Reflex Arc

Make sure you also learn the ***BLOCK DIAGRAM*** of a reflex arc.
The block diagram is really just the bits in the *rectangular boxes*.
The pictures are there to help show what it all means — and to jolly it up a bit:

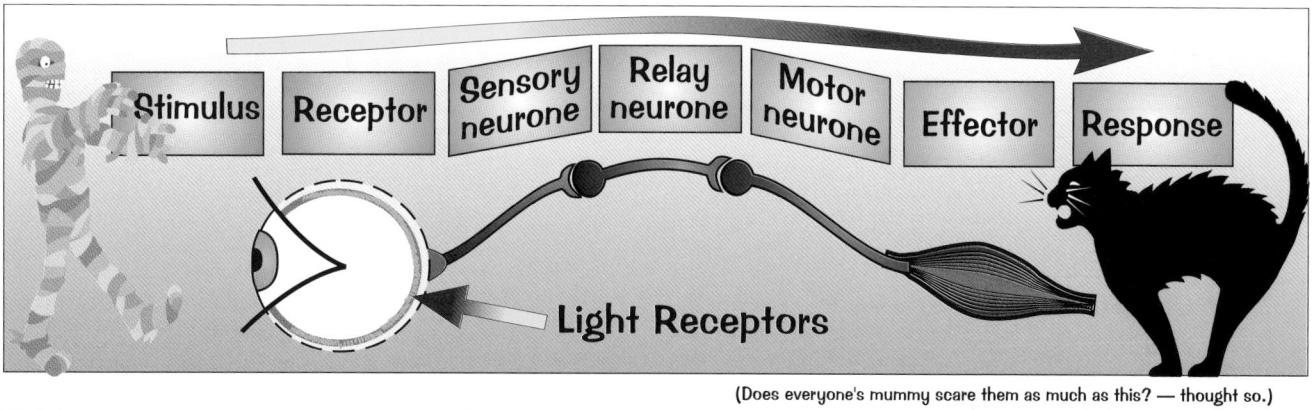

(Does everyone's mummy scare them as much as this? — thought so.)

Reflexes — they can really get on your nerves...

The reflex arc isn't so bad really, so long as you take the time to learn all the little bits and bobs that go with it. They could cheerfully ask you to write down the block diagram for a reflex arc and you've got to be able to fill in all the right bits — in the right order. *Learn and scribble*...

The Eye

Learn The Eye with all its labels:

1) The pupil is the hole in the middle of the iris, which the light goes through.

2) The aqueous humour is a clear liquid and the vitreous humour is a clear jelly.

3) The aqueous humour and vitreous humour support the spherical shape of the eye.

4) The retina is the light sensitive part. It has light receptors all over it, except at the blind spot where the optic nerve is.

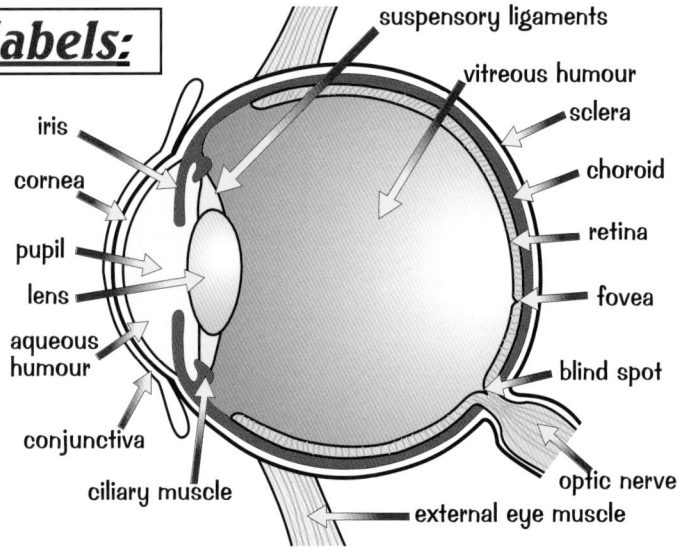

Adjusting for Light and Dark — the IRIS

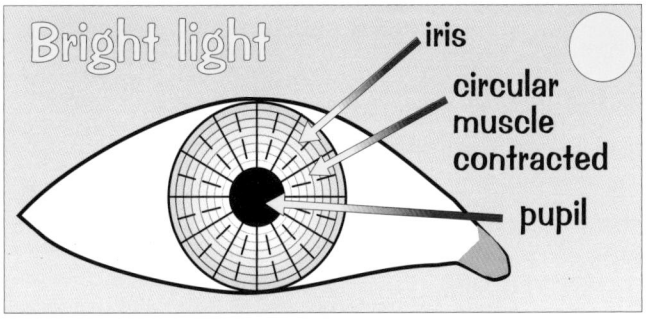

1) The CIRCULAR MUSCLES contract.
2) The iris closes up, the pupil gets SMALLER.
3) LESS LIGHT gets into the eye.

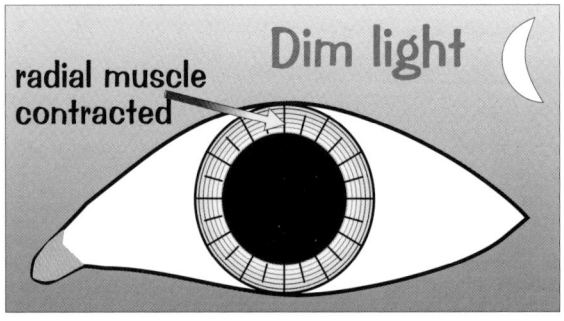

1) The RADIAL MUSCLES contract.
2) The iris opens out, the pupil gets BIGGER.
3) This lets MORE LIGHT into the eye.

Focusing on Near and Distant Objects

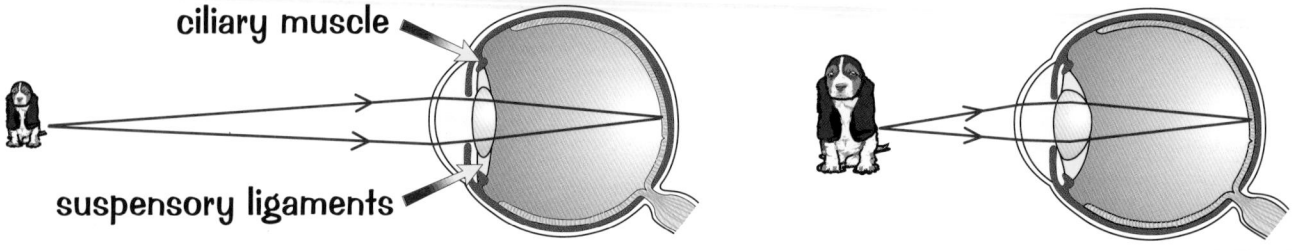

TO LOOK AT DISTANT OBJECTS:
1) The ciliary muscles RELAX, which allows the suspensory ligaments to PULL TIGHT.
2) This makes the lens go THIN.

TO LOOK AT NEAR OBJECTS:
1) The ciliary muscles CONTRACT which SLACKENS the suspensory ligaments.
2) The lens becomes FAT.

Let's See What You've Learned Then...

This is a pretty straightforward page of information. You need to make sure you know all the diagrams with all labels and also the numbered points for each.
Practise until you can scribble the whole lot down from memory.

Revision Summary for Section Two

Phew, there's a lot of stuff to learn in Section Two. And it's all that grisly "open heart surgery" type stuff too, with all those gory diagrams. Mind you, it's all fairly straightforward and factual — you know, nothing difficult to understand, just lots of facts to learn. And lots of gory diagrams. You know the big plan with these questions though. Keep practising till you can whizz them all off without a moment's hesitation on any of them. It's a nice trick if you can do it.

1) Write down the seven types of nutrient needed in a balanced diet.
2) Say what kind of foods each one is found in, and what the nutrient is needed for.
3) Sketch a diagram of the digestive system and put the ten labels on it.
4) Write down at least two details for eight of the ten labelled parts.
5) What *exactly* do enzymes do in the digestive system?
6) List the three main digestive enzymes, which foods they act on, and what they produce.
7) Draw a full diagram of a single tooth, and one of the jaw showing all four types of teeth.
8) Describe what each of the four types of teeth are used for.
9) Draw a diagram of a peristaltic squeeze and label the different types of tissue, with their use.
10) Sketch a villus, and say what it's for. Point out the three main features of villi.
11) What are the three "big" food molecules, and which kind of foods are each of them found in?
12) What small molecules are they each broken down into in the digestive system?
13) Sketch a diagram showing what then happens to the small molecules.
14) Describe the symptoms of a lack of: a) protein b) iron c) calcium d) vitamin C e) vitamin D.
15) Detail the four boring food tests: a) starch b) protein c) simple sugars d) fats.
16) Draw a diagram of the human circulatory system: heart, lungs, arteries, veins, etc.
17) Explain why it is a *double* circulatory system, and describe the pressure and oxygen content of the blood in each bit. What are the big words for saying if the blood has oxygen in or not?
18) Draw a full diagram of the heart with all the labels. Explain how the two halves differ.
19) How do ventricles and atria compare, and why? What are the valves for?
20) Describe briefly with diagrams the three stages of the pumping cycle for the heart.
21) Sketch an artery, a capillary, and a vein, with labels, and explain the features of all three.
22) Sketch a red blood cell and a white blood cell and give five details about each.
23) Sketch some blood plasma. List all the things that are carried in the plasma (around 10).
24) Sketch some platelets. What do they do all day?
25) Draw a diagram of the thorax, showing all the breathing equipment.
26) Describe what happens during breathing in and breathing out. Be sure to give all the details.
27) Where are alveoli found? How big are they and what are they for? Give four features.
28) Explain what happens to oxygen and carbon dioxide, in the alveoli and also at the body cells.
29) What is respiration? Give a proper definition.
30) What is the composition of inhaled and exhaled air? Give two comments on the difference.
31) What is "aerobic respiration"? Give the equation for it.
32) What is "anaerobic respiration"? Give the equation for what happens in our bodies.
33) What is meant by the oxygen debt? What is a good measure of fitness?
34) What is the word equation for fermentation? What two products use fermentation?
35) Draw a diagram showing the main parts of the nervous system.
36) List the five sense organs and say what kind of receptors each one has.
37) What are effectors? What two things constitute the central nervous system?
38) What are the three types of neurone? Draw a detailed diagram of a typical neurone.
39) Describe how a reflex arc works and why it's a good thing. Draw a block diagram for it.
40) Draw a full diagram of an eye with all labels and details.
41) Describe how the eye adjusts for light and dark, and to focus on near and distant objects.

Hormones

Hormones are Chemical Messengers sent in the Blood

1) Hormones are CHEMICALS released DIRECTLY INTO THE BLOOD.
2) They are carried in the BLOOD PLASMA to other parts of the body.
3) They are produced in various GLANDS (endocrine glands) as shown on the diagram.
4) They TRAVEL ALL OVER THE BODY but only affect PARTICULAR CELLS in particular places.
5) The cells they affect are called TARGET CELLS.
6) They travel at "THE SPEED OF BLOOD".
7) They have LONG-LASTING EFFECTS.
8) They control things that need CONSTANT ADJUSTMENT.

LEARN THIS DEFINITION:

HORMONES ...
are chemical messengers which travel in the blood to activate target cells.

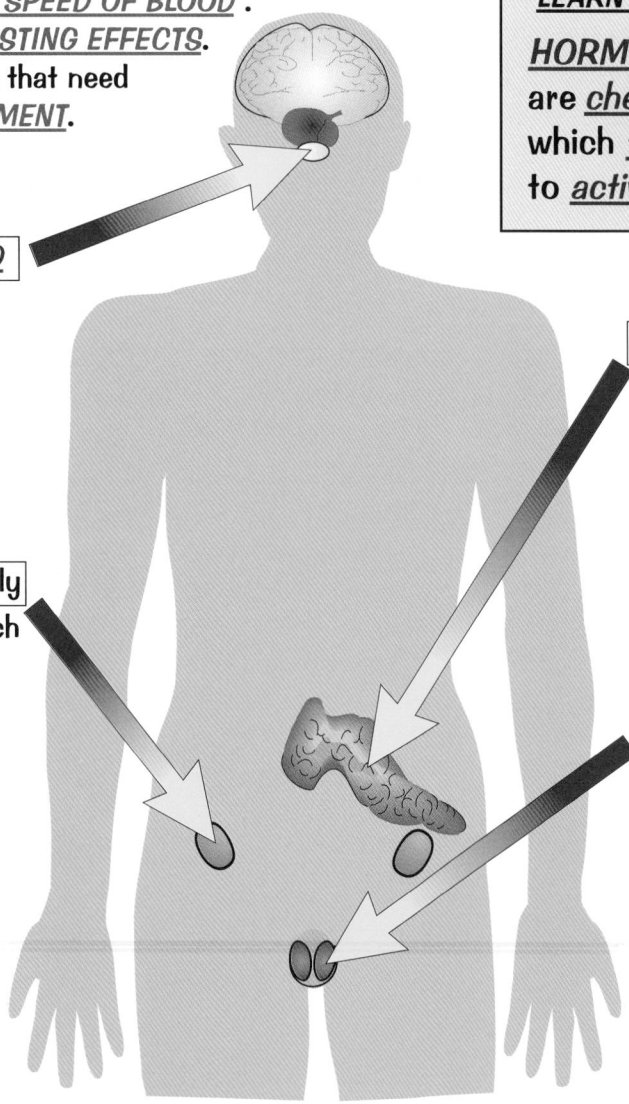

THE PITUITARY GLAND
This produces many important hormones, mostly for controlling other glands.

PANCREAS
Produces insulin for the control of blood sugar.
(If you're doing NEAB it also produces glucagon.)

OVARIES — females only
Produce oestrogen which promotes all female secondary sexual characteristics during puberty:
1) Extra hair in places.
2) Changes in body proportions.
3) Egg production.

TESTES — males only
Produce testosterone which promotes all male secondary sexual characteristics at puberty:
1) Extra hair in places.
2) Changes in body proportions.
3) Sperm production.

Hormones and Nerves do Similar Jobs, but there are Important Differences

NERVES:
1) Very FAST message.
2) Act for a very SHORT TIME.
3) Act on a very PRECISE AREA.
4) IMMEDIATE reaction.

HORMONES:
1) SLOWER message.
2) Act for a LONG TIME.
3) Act in a more GENERAL way.
4) LONGER-TERM reaction.

Hormones — Easy peasy...

Well let's face it, there's not much to learn here is there? The diagram and all its labels are easy enough, and so's the comparison of nerves and hormones. The definition of hormones is worth learning word for word. The eight points at the top of the page are best done with the good old "mini-essay" method. Learn it, cover the page and scribble. Then try again. And smile of course.

Insulin and Diabetes

Insulin is a hormone which controls how much sugar there is in your blood. LEARN how it does it:

Insulin Controls Blood Sugar Levels

1) Eating carbohydrate foods puts a lot of glucose into the blood from the gut.
2) Normal metabolism of cells removes glucose from the blood.
3) Vigorous exercise removes much more glucose from the blood.
4) Obviously, to keep the level of blood glucose controlled there has to be a way to add or remove glucose from the blood. And this is it:

Blood glucose level TOO HIGH — insulin is ADDED

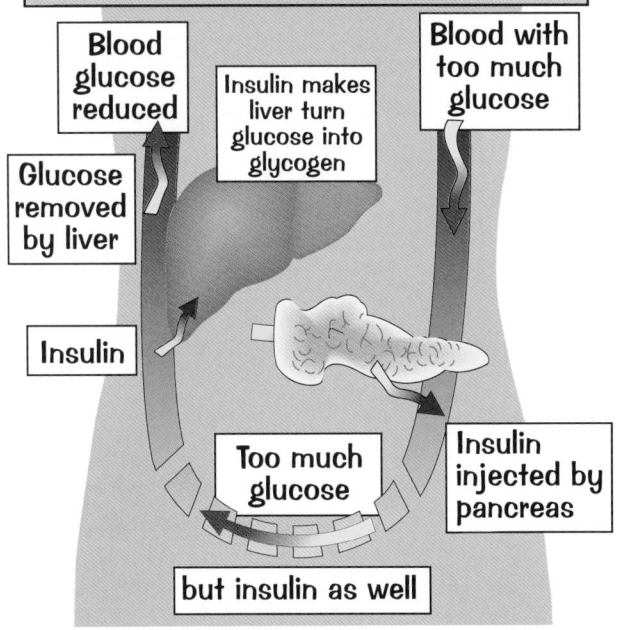

Blood glucose level TOO LOW — insulin is NOT ADDED

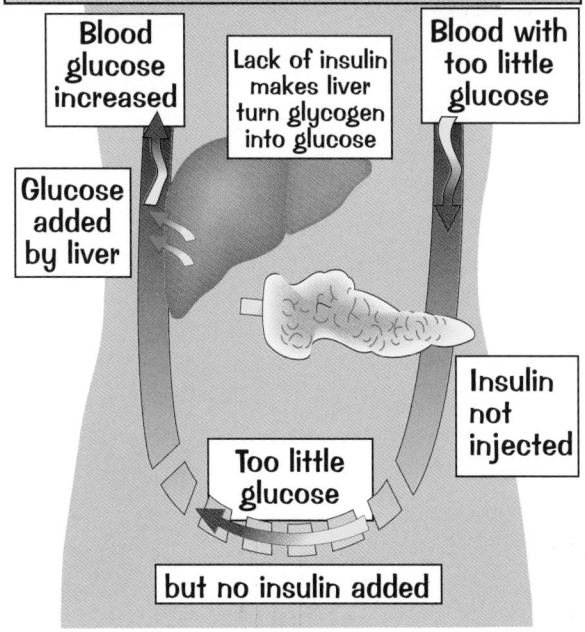

Remember, the addition of insulin reduces blood sugar level.
(For NEAB syllabuses you also need to know that when the blood sugar is too low, another hormone called Glucagon is added instead of insulin. Glucagon makes the liver release glucose into the blood.)

Diabetes — the Pancreas Stops Making Enough Insulin

1) Diabetes is a disease in which the pancreas doesn't produce enough insulin.
2) The result is that a person's blood sugar can rise to a level that can kill them.
3) The problem can be controlled in two ways:

A) Avoiding foods rich in carbohydrate (which turns to glucose when digested).
It can also be helpful to take exercise after eating carbohydrates... i.e. trying to use up the extra glucose by doing physical activity, but this isn't usually very practical.

B) Injecting insulin into the blood before meals, (especially if high in carbohydrates).
This will make the liver remove the glucose from the blood as soon as it enters it from the gut, when the (carbohydrate-rich) food is being digested. This stops the level of glucose in the blood from getting too high and is a very effective treatment.

Learn all this stuff about blood sugar and diabetes...

This stuff on blood sugar and insulin can seem a bit confusing at first, but if you concentrate on learning those two diagrams, it'll all start to get a lot easier. Don't forget that only carbohydrate foods put the blood sugar levels up. Learn it all, then cover the page and scribble it all down.

Female Menstrual Cycle

The Menstrual Cycle has Four Stages

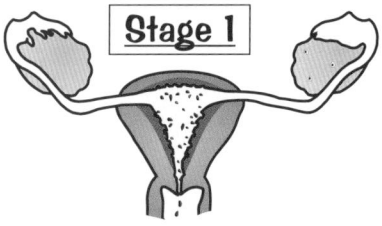

STAGE 1

Day 1 is when the Bleeding Starts

The uterus lining *breaks down* slowly over a period of about *four days*. This results in "*bleeding*" from the vagina as all the remains of the lining steadily emerge.

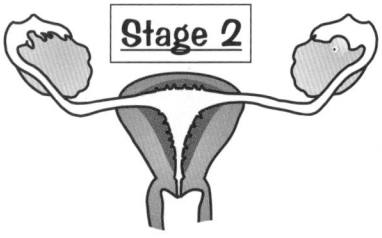

STAGE 2

The Lining of the Womb Builds up Again

From *day 4* to *day 14*, the lining of the womb is *built up* into a *thick spongy layer* of blood vessels ready to receive a *fertilised egg*.

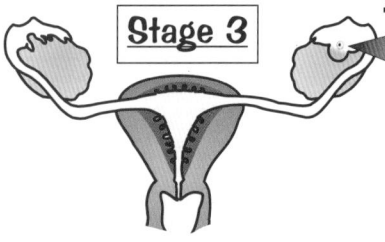

STAGE 3

An Egg is Released at Day 14

The egg develops in the *ovary* and is *released* at *day 14* of the cycle.

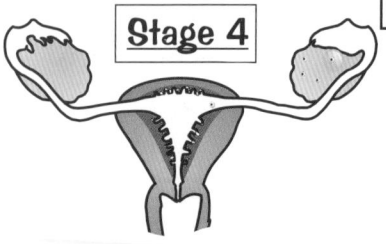

STAGE 4

The Wall is then Maintained for 14 Days

The thickened lining of the womb is *maintained* for about *14 days*, until *day 28*. If no fertilised egg has landed on the uterus wall by day 28 then the spongy lining starts to *break down again* and the whole cycle *starts over*. The diagram below shows the whole thing.

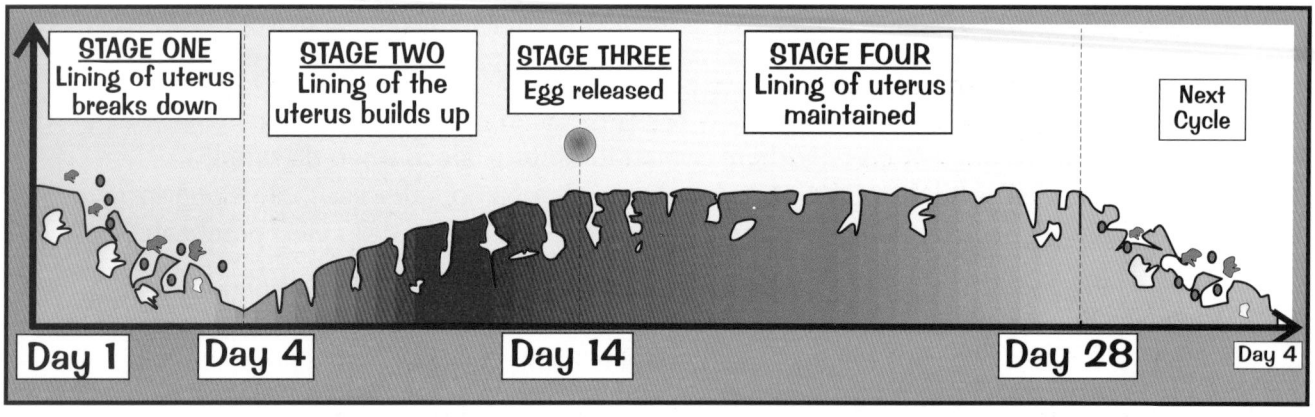

Female or otherwise, you've still gotta learn it...

This is the relatively simple stuff on the menstrual cycle and it's definitely well worth learning. Make sure you know what all the four stages in the cycle are. Then *cover the page* and try to *scribble down* all the diagrams and the words that go with them. Then try again. *And enjoy*.

Hormones in the Menstrual Cycle

Oestrogen and Progesterone are The Two Main Hormones

These two hormones are produced in the *ovaries* and they control the main events of the cycle:

1) OESTROGEN:

1) Causes the *lining of the uterus* to *thicken* and *grow*.
2) Stimulates the *release of an egg* at day 14.

2) PROGESTERONE:

1) *Maintains the lining* of the uterus.
When the level of progesterone *falls*, the lining *breaks down*.

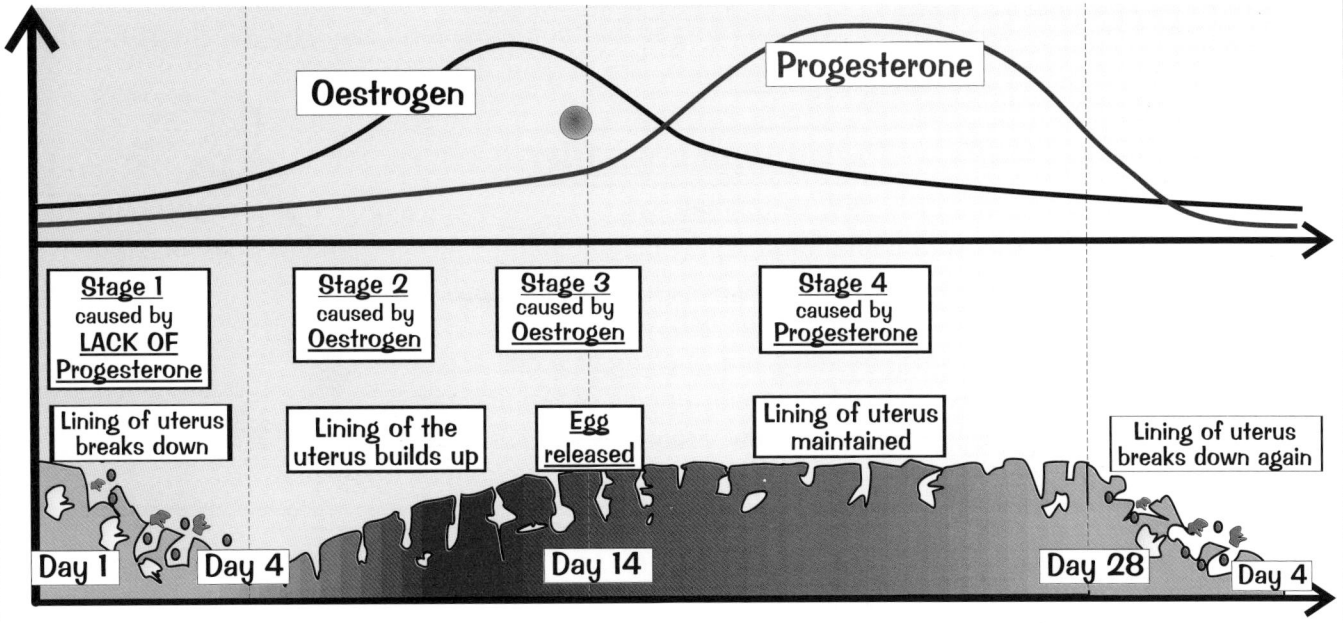

Female Hormones are Used to Control Babies

1) To Stimulate Egg Production in Fertility Treatment

1) When couples are trying for babies and it doesn't seem to be happening, there are quite a few new *fertility treatments* that can be employed.

2) One of the simplest is prescribing a *hormone* which can be taken by women to stimulate *egg production* in their *ovaries*.

3) This can work very well but they have to be very *careful* with the *dosage* or you get too many eggs being released all at once. This results in *multiple births*.

2) To Stop Egg Production in The CONTRACEPTIVE PILL

1) "*THE PILL*", as it's cheerfully known, contains both *progesterone* and *oestrogen*.

2) If *oestrogen* is taken *every day* to keep the level of it *permanently high*, then after a while egg production *stops* and stays stopped.

The Menstrual Cycle — isn't it complicated...

It's quite tricky remembering the names of these two hormones, and it's even trickier remembering exactly what they do in the menstrual cycle. But it can be done. You've just gotta keep trying. Also learn which hormones are used to control babies. One treatment increases the chance of getting pregnant, and the other reduces it. *Learn, cover, scribble, etc...*

Disease in Humans

There are Two types of Microbes: Bacteria and Viruses

Microbes are organisms which get inside you and make you feel ill. There are two main types:

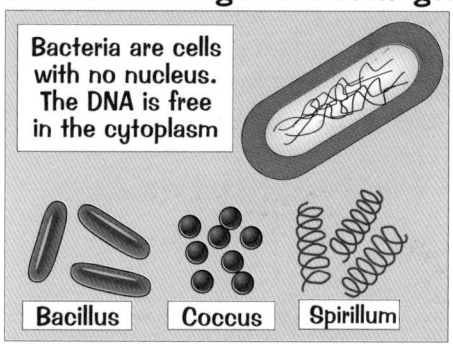

Bacteria are Very Small Living Cells

1) These are *very small cells*, (about 1/100th the size of your body cells), which reproduce rapidly inside your body.
2) They make you *feel ill* by doing *two* things:
   a) *damaging your cells* b) *producing toxins*.
3) Don't forget that some bacteria are *useful* if they're in the *right place*, like in your digestive system.

Viruses are not cells — they're much smaller

1) These are *not cells*. They are *very very small*, about 1/100th the size of a bacterium.
2) They are no more than a *coat of protein* around a *DNA strand*.
3) They make you feel ill by *damaging your cells*.
4) They *replicate themselves* by invading the *nucleus* of a cell and using the *DNA* it contains to produce many *copies* of themselves.
5) The cell then *bursts*, releasing all the new viruses.
6) In this way they can reproduce *very quickly*.

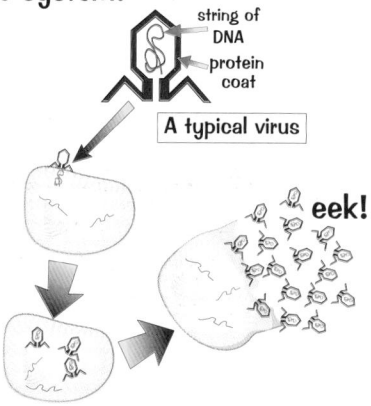

Five ways that microbes can enter our bodies

Microbes can enter our bodies in five ways, but we do have some *defences*.

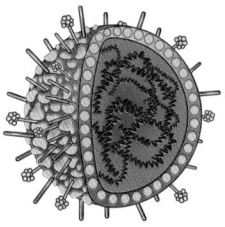
A horrid Flu Virus

1) Through the Skin and Eyes

Undamaged skin is a very effective barrier against microbes. If it gets damaged, the blood *clots* quickly to *seal cuts* and keep the microbes out. *Eyes* produce a chemical which *kills bacteria* on the surface of the eye.

2) Through the Digestive System

Contaminated food and *dirty water* allow microbes to enter your body. The stomach produces strong *hydrochloric acid* which *kills* most microbes which enter that way.

3) Through the Respiratory System

The whole *respiratory tract* (nasal passage, trachea and lungs) is lined with *mucus* and *cilia* which catch *dust* and *bacteria* before they reach the lungs.

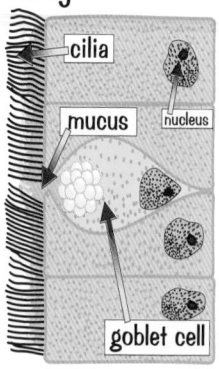

4) Through the Reproductive System

Several diseases can be caught during sexual intercourse and our bodies have *few defences* against infection from such activities.

5) Through Vectors (e.g. mosquitos, fleas)

Vectors are *organisms* which *carry disease* from one person to another. For example the *mosquito* carries *malaria* from *person to person* when it stops to suck their *blood*. Unfortunately we have *no natural protection* against insects *spitting* into our *bloodstream*. *The black death*, which killed over *a quarter* of the entire population of *Europe* in the 1300s was carried from *person to person* by the *fleas* that live on *rats*. We don't tolerate rats any more, they're bad news.

(Apart from Adele's pet ones)

Fighting Disease

Once microbes have entered our bodies they will *reproduce rapidly* unless they are *destroyed*. Your "*immune system*" does just that, and *white blood cells* are the most important part of it.

Your Immune System: White blood cells

They *travel around* in your blood and *crawl into every part of you*, constantly *patrolling* for microbes. When they come across an invading *microbe* they have *three lines of attack*:

1) Consuming Them

White blood cells can *engulf* foreign cells and *digest* them.

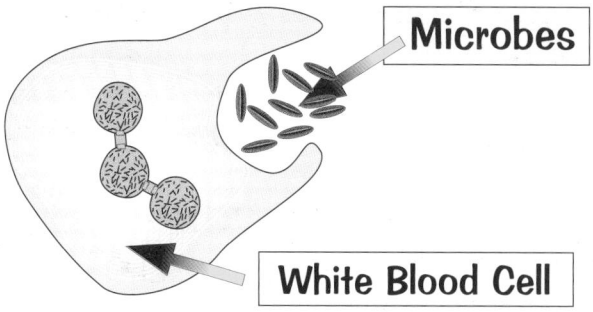

2) Producing Antibodies

When your white blood cells come across a *foreign cell* they will *start to produce* chemicals called *antibodies* to kill the new invading cells. The antibodies are then produced *rapidly* and flow *all round the body* to kill all *similar* bacteria or viruses.

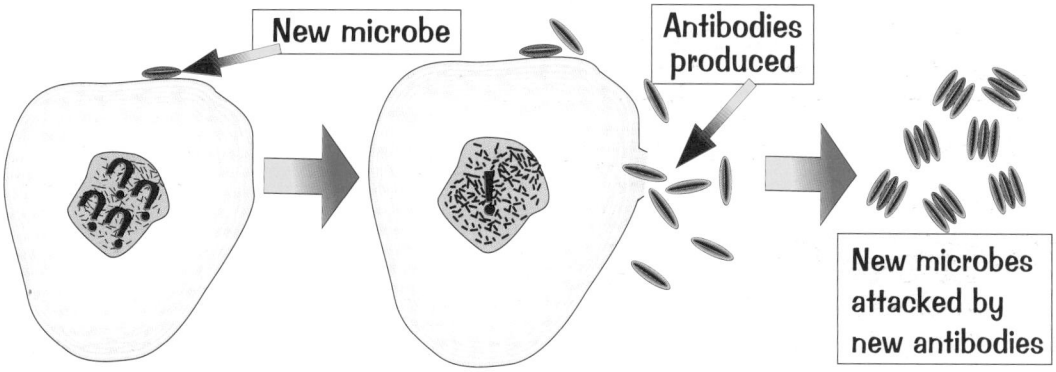

3) Producing Antitoxins

Antitoxins counter the effect of any *poisons* (toxins) produced by the *invading bacteria*.

Antibiotics kill Bacteria but NOT Viruses

1) *Antibiotics* are *drugs* that kill *bacteria* without killing your own body cells.

2) They are *very useful* for clearing up infections that your body is having *trouble* with.

3) However they don't kill *viruses*.
Flu and colds are caused by *viruses* and basically, *you're on your own*, pal.

4) There are *no drugs* to kill *viruses* and you just have to *wait* for your body to deal with it and *suffer* in the meantime.

5) Still, it's better than being bitten by a rat flea.

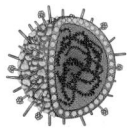
A horrid Flu Virus

An even more horrid Rat Flea

It's Grisly Stuff, but worth learning just the Same...

Two pages this time, and definitely 'mini-essay' material. There are four main sections, with several subsections. Do a *mini-essay* on each subsection and then *check* what you forgot.

Drugs

1) Drugs are substances which alter the way the body works. Some drugs are useful of course, for example antibiotics such as penicillin. However there are many drugs which are dangerous if misused, and many of them are addictive or "habit-forming".
2) The loss of control and judgement caused by many drugs can easily lead to death from various other causes, e.g. choking on vomit, falling down stairs, passing under vehicles, etc.

There are two types of Addiction — Chemical and Psychological

1) There's a difference between true chemical addiction and just psychological addiction.
2) In chemical addiction the body becomes adjusted to the constant presence of the drug in the system. If the drug is withdrawn, there are various unpleasant physical withdrawal symptoms: fevers, hallucinations, nausea, and the shakes.
3) Psychological addiction is where the person "feels the need" to keep taking the drug.

Stimulants

1) Stimulants tend to make the nervous system generally more alert and "awake".
2) Caffeine is a mild stimulant found in tea and coffee. It's pretty harmless. Few lives are wrecked by obsessive tea-drinking.
3) However, amphetamine and methedrine are also stimulants.
4) Strong stimulants like these produce a feeling of boundless energy, but the person experiences serious depression if they stop taking it, so an unhealthy dependence develops all too easily. Continued use can lead to hallucinations and changes in personality.

Hallucinogens — LSD and Ecstasy

1) LSD is hallucinogenic, i.e. it causes hallucinations.
2) Ecstasy is hallucinogenic in high doses, but in smaller amounts gives a feeling of boundless energy similar to that from amphetamines, together with the same serious problem of a growing dependence.
3) The feeling of energy leads to a danger of overheating and collapse through dehydration.

Depressants slow down your responses — Alcohol and Barbiturates

Depressants tend to slow down the responses of the nervous system, causing slow reactions and poor judgement of speed, distances, etc. See "Alcohol" on the next page.

Pain Killers — Aspirin, Heroin and Morphine

1) Heroin is a particularly nasty drug causing a serious deterioration in personality and as the addiction grows the person's whole life degenerates into a desperate struggle to obtain money for their daily heroin requirement, often resulting in a sad life of crime to pay for it.
2) Morphine is also highly addictive.
3) Aspirin is a useful painkiller for many minor illnesses, but its overuse has harmful effects.

Solvents

1) Solvents are found in a variety of "household" items e.g. glues, paints, etc.
2) They are dangerous and have many damaging effects on your body and personality.
3) They cause hallucinations and adversely affect personality and behaviour.
4) They cause damage to the lungs, brain, liver and kidney.

Learn about these drugs and then forget them...

Anyone with half a brain avoids these drugs like they do rat fleas.
Enjoy your life, instead of being a sucker.

Alcohol and Tobacco

1) Alcohol and tobacco are the two main (non-medical) drugs which are legal in this country.
2) But don't be fooled. They can do you a lot of harm just like the other drugs can.

Alcohol

1) The main effect of alcohol is to reduce the activity of the nervous system. The positive aspect of this is that it makes us feel less inhibited, and there's no doubt that alcohol in moderation helps people to socialise and relax with each other.
2) However, if you let alcohol take over, it can wreck your life. And it does. It wrecks a lot of people's lives. You've got to control it.
3) Once alcohol starts to take over someone's life there are many harmful effects:
   a) Alcohol is basically poisonous. Too much drinking will cause severe damage to the liver and the brain leading to liver disease and a noticeable drop in brain function.
   b) Too much alcohol impairs judgement which can cause accidents, and it can also severely affect the person's work and home life.
   c) Serious dependency on alcohol can eventually lead to loss of job, loss of income and the start of a severe downward spiral.

Smoking Tobacco

Smoking is no good to anyone. It doesn't have any positive social aspects and is without any doubt at all a very serious cause of ill health.
And once you've started smoking there's no going back. It's a one way trip pal.

And you'll notice that smokers are no happier than non-smokers, even when they're smoking. What may start off as something "different" to do, rapidly becomes something they have to do, just to feel OK. But non-smokers feel just as OK without spending £20 or more each week and wrecking their health into the bargain.

And why do people start smoking? To look the part, that's why. They have an image in their head of how they want to appear and smoking seems the perfect fashion accessory.

Well just remember, it's a one way trip. You might think it makes you look cool at 16, but will it still seem the perfect fashion accessory when you're 20 with a new group of friends who don't smoke? Nope. Too late. You're stuck with it.

And by the time you're 60 it'll have cost you over £40,000. Enough to buy a Ferrari or a new house. That's quite an expensive fashion accessory.
Smoking? Cool? Oh yeah — it's about as cool as cool can be, I'd say.

Oh and by the way...

Tobacco smoke does this inside your body:
1) It coats the inside of your lungs with tar so they become hideously inefficient.
2) It covers the cilia in tar preventing them from getting bacteria out of your lungs.
3) It causes disease of the heart and blood vessels, leading to heart attacks and strokes.
4) It causes lung cancer. Out of every ten lung cancer patients, nine of them smoke.
5) It causes severe loss of lung function leading to diseases like emphysema and bronchitis, in which the inside of the lungs is basically wrecked. People with severe bronchitis can't manage even a brisk walk, because their lungs can't get enough oxygen into the blood. It eventually kills over 20,000 people in Britain every year.
6) But this is the best bit. The effect of the nicotine is negligible — other than to make you addicted to it. It doesn't make you high — just dependent. Great. Fantastic.

Learn the Numbered Points for your Exam...

It's the disease aspects they concentrate on most in the Exams. Learn the rest for a nice life.

Homeostasis

1) *Homeostasis* is a fancy word.
2) It covers a lot of things, so I guess it has to be. Homeostasis covers all the functions of your body which try to maintain a "*constant internal environment*". Learn the definition:

HOMEOSTASIS:
The maintenance of a CONSTANT INTERNAL ENVIRONMENT

There are Six Different Bodily Levels that need to be Controlled:

1) REMOVAL OF CO_2
2) REMOVAL OF *UREA*

⇐ These two are *WASTES*. They're constantly produced in the body and *you just need to get rid of them*.

3) *ION* content
4) *WATER* content
5) *SUGAR* content
6) *TEMPERATURE*

⇐ These four are all "*GOODIES*" and we need them, *BUT AT JUST THE RIGHT LEVEL* — not too much and not too little.

All the Cells in your Body are Bathed in Tissue Fluid

All your body's cells are *BATHED IN TISSUE FLUID*, which is just *blood plasma* which has leaked out of the capillaries (on purpose).

To keep all your cells working properly, *this fluid must be JUST RIGHT* — in other words, *THE SIX THINGS* above must all be *KEPT AT THE RIGHT LEVEL* — not too high, and not too low.

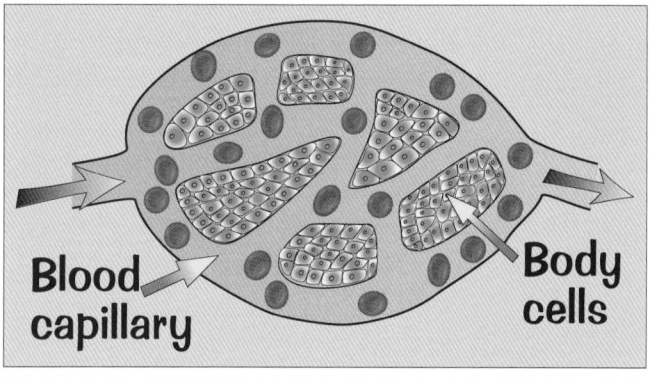

There are Three Main Things that Skin does for you:

Well, talk about "*maintaining a constant internal environment*" (as you do). It'd be pretty tricky without *skin* wouldn't it.

1) It stops you *DRYING UP* (*DEHYDRATING*).
2) It keeps *GERMS OUT*.
3) It helps control your *TEMPERATURE*.

The first two are really pretty obvious. The skin is a waterproof, germproof, nearly-everything-that's-not-too-sharp-or-hot-or-moving-too-fast-proof layer that keeps the rest of the world out and so maintains your precious "*constant internal environment*" so all your little cells can carry on their daily business in warmth and comfort.

(This is starting to remind me of a school, with you lot as the cells, being kept warm, well fed, freshly watered, and constantly supplied with all the stuff you need to carry on your daily "work" — gee, it's kinda like "Homeostasis High".)

Learn about Homeostasis — and keep your cool...

This is all a bit technical. Homeostasis is really quite a complicated business. It's just a good job it does it automatically or we'd all be in real trouble. You still gotta *learn it* for your Exam though. *Scribble*.

Organs Involved in Homeostasis

You need to know which *organs* are involved in keeping your *internal environment* OK.
Learn this diagram with all the labels:

Learn the Organs Involved in Homeostasis:

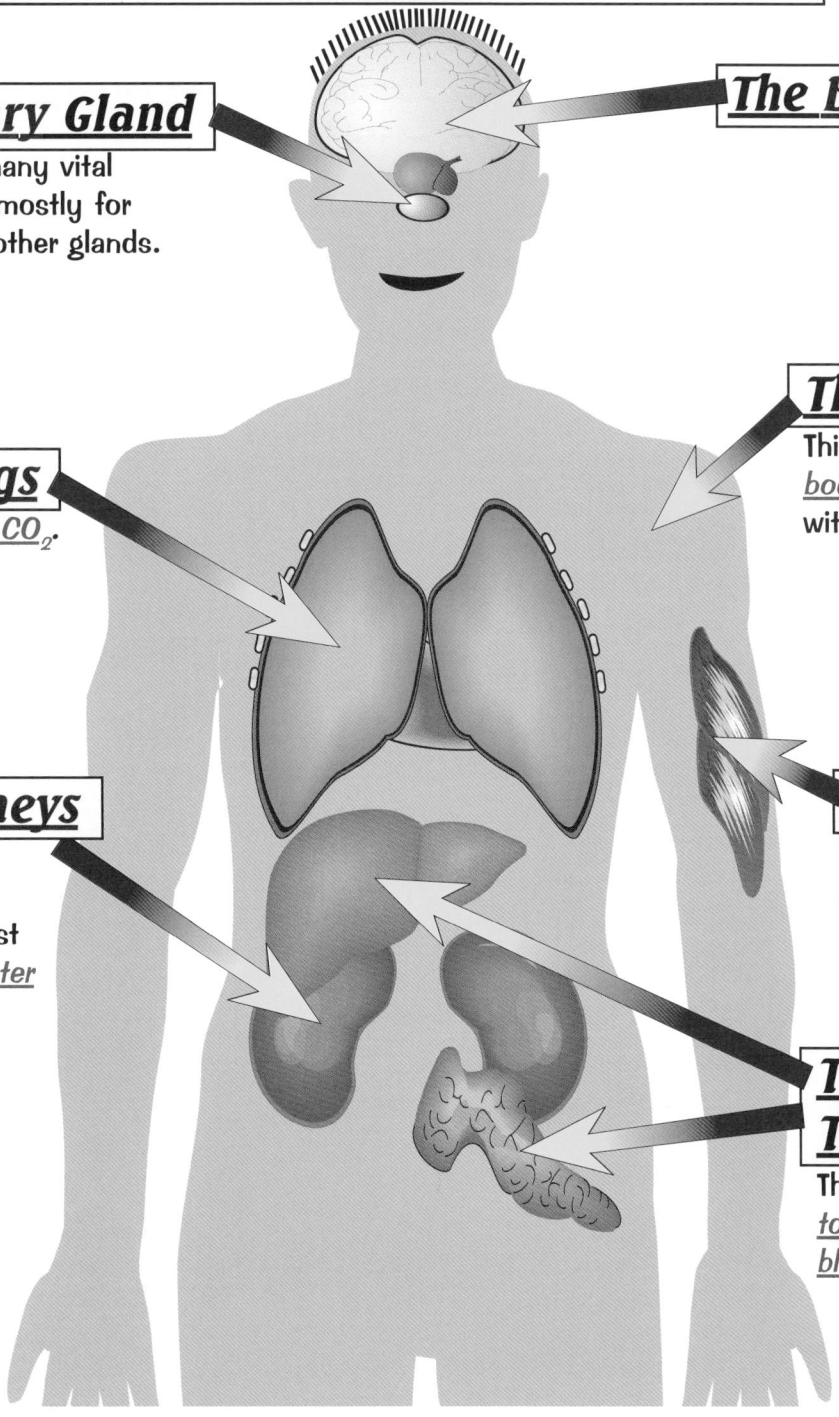

Pituitary Gland
Produces many vital hormones, mostly for controlling other glands.

The Brain

The Skin
This adjusts the *body temperature*, with the help of...

The Lungs
These *remove CO_2*.

The Kidneys
These remove urea.
They also adjust the *ion* and *water content* of the blood.

The Muscles
which can produce *heat* if necessary (by *shivering*).

The Liver
The Pancreas
These two *work together* to adjust *blood sugar level*.

Fingers *not* needed for homeostasis.

I hope you've clocked on that this diagram is different to the one on P. 40.
That one shows where *hormones* are produced.
This one shows which organs keep the inside of your body nicely in balance — *homeostasis*.

Be like Old Mr Wurlitzer — know your organs...

Well, that's certainly a nice big diagram if ever there was one. See if you can spot the eight organs involved in maintaining your internal environment. Then learn the diagram with all the details. *Cover the page* and *scribble it all down*. Geesh, it is a big diagram isn't it. Marvellous.

Kidneys

Kidneys basically act as filters to "clean the blood"

1) You have *two kidneys*.
2) Their job is to "*filter*" the blood to keep it just how it should be.
3) The wastes from the kidneys are stored in your bladder (urine) and you get rid of it all every now and then.
3) There are *three things* in particular that the kidneys remove from the blood. Read on...

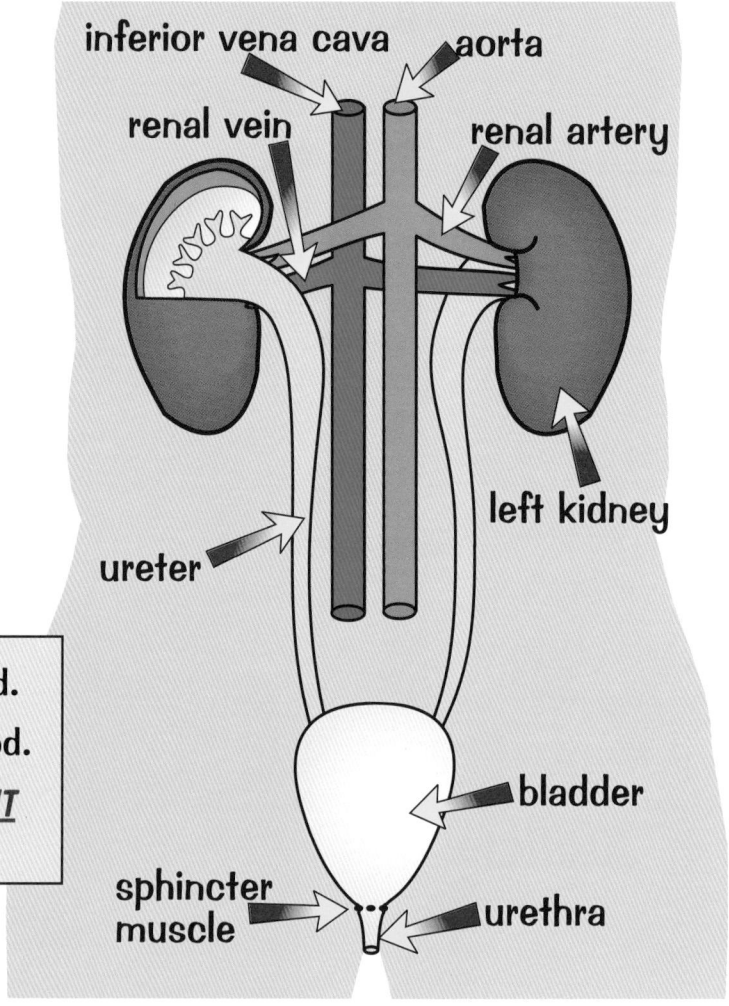

The Kidneys Perform Three Main Functions:

1) *REMOVAL OF UREA* from the blood.
2) *ADJUSTMENT OF IONS* in the blood.
3) *ADJUSTMENT OF WATER CONTENT* of the blood.

1) Removal of Urea, which is a Poison

1) *Urea* is produced in the *liver*.
2) Proteins can't be *stored* by the body so *excess amino acids* are *broken down* by the liver into fats and carbohydrates.
3) The *waste product* is *urea* which is passed into the blood to be *filtered out* by the *kidneys*. Urea is also lost partly in *sweat*.
4) Urea is *poisonous*.

2) Adjustment of Ion Content — things like Salt

1) *Ions*, such as sodium (Na^+) are taken into the body in *food*, and then absorbed into the blood.
2) If the food contains *too much* of any ions then the excess ions are *removed* by the kidneys. For example, a salty meal will contain far too much Na^+ and the kidneys will *remove the excess* from the blood.
3) Some ions are also lost in *sweat* (which tastes salty, you'll have noticed).
4) But the important thing to remember is that the *balance* is always maintained by the *kidneys*.

The wastes from the kidneys become *urine*. The *amount* of urine and the *colour* of it (i.e. its *concentration*) depend on *how much water is taken out*. That depends on quite a few factors...

Kidneys

3) Adjustment of Water Content

1) Water is *taken in* to the body as *food and drink*.
2) Water is *lost* from the body in *four ways*:

1) in *URINE*	2) in *FAECES*	3) in *SWEAT*	4) in *BREATH*

The body needs to *constantly balance* the water *COMING IN* against the water *GOING OUT*.
The *water balance* is between these three simple things:

1) Liquids *consumed*
2) Amount *sweated out*
3) Amount *dumped by the kidneys* in the *urine*.

ON A COLD DAY: If you *don't sweat*, you'll produce *more urine* which will be *pale and dilute*.

ON A HOT DAY: You *sweat a lot*, your urine will be *dark-coloured*, *concentrated* and *little of it*.

This is assuming that you don't *drink* any differently.
It's pretty obvious that if you *drink more* you'll *wee more* — and if you don't, you won't.

Kidney Failure: The Two Treatments

1) Dialysis by Kidney Machine

1) Blood is *taken from an arm* and passed through a tube *bathed in a fluid* a bit like *blood plasma*.
2) *Urea* and other wastes then *diffuse out* of the blood, which then *returns to the arm*.
3) This has to be done for *12-18 hours every week*.
4) The treatment is *expensive*.

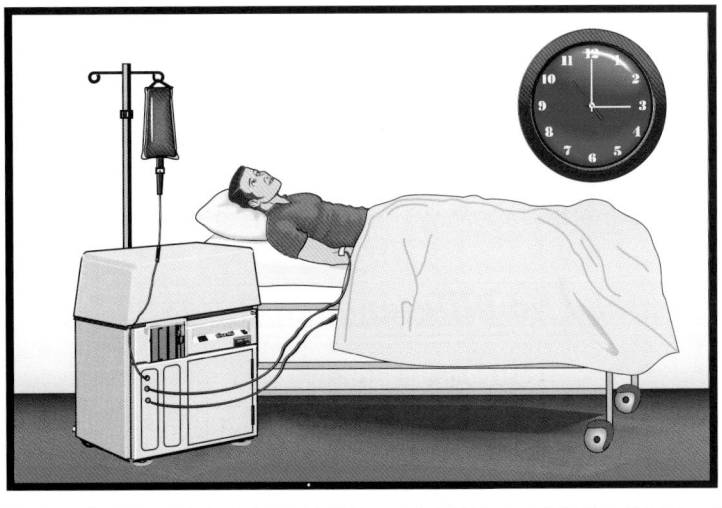

2) Kidney Transplant

1) A *healthy kidney* from a person *recently dead* or a *living relative* is "plumbed in".
2) The *blood groups* for the two people must be the *same*.
3) Ideally the *tissue types* should also be the same — if so the *success rate* is *80%*.
4) *Anti-rejection* drugs and *antibiotics* must be taken for the *rest of their life*.

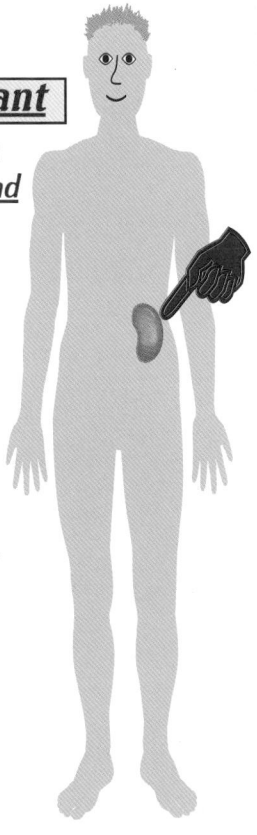

Phew — taking the mickey is much less complicated...

I tell you what, there's some stuff on these two pages. Definitely a case for the very exciting mini-essay method. Learn the five headings, then *cover the page*, write them down, and then *scribble a mini-essay* for each one. Then look back and see what you missed.
Then try again. And learn the diagrams as well, until you can scribble them down effortlessly.

Control of Body Temperature

1) The *ENZYMES* in the cells of the human body works best at 37°C.
2) *THE SKIN* then has *three tricks* for *controlling body temperature*:

The Skin has Three Tricks for Altering Body Temperature

When you're TOO HOT:

1) *HAIRS* lie flat.
2) *SWEAT* is produced to cool you down.
3) The *BLOOD SUPPLY* to the skin opens up to release body heat. This is called *vasodilation*.

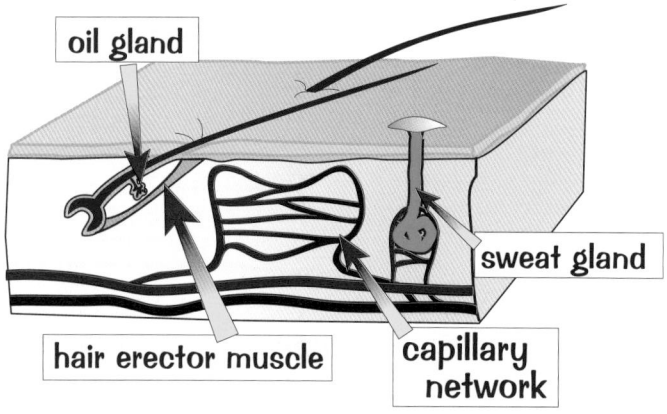

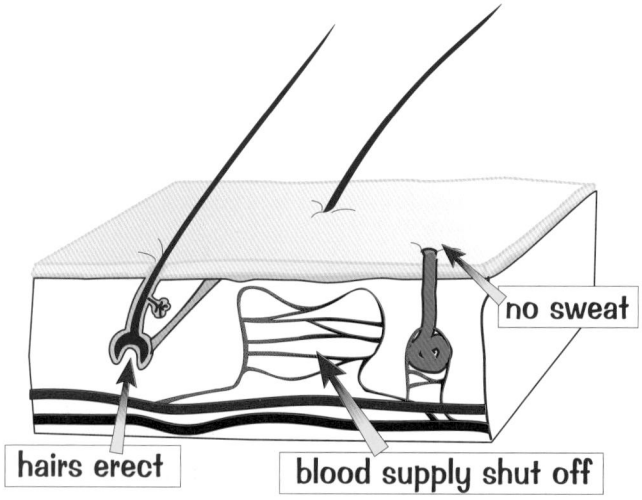

When you're TOO COLD:

1) *HAIRS* stand on end to keep you warm.
2) *NO SWEAT* is produced.
3) The *BLOOD SUPPLY* to the skin *CLOSES OFF*. This is called *vasoconstriction*.

When you are Cold your Body Increases its Metabolism

Your body can produce extra heat when needed. It does this in two ways:

1) By *INCREASING LIVER ACTIVITY*
2) By *SHIVERING*.

Both of these *GENERATE HEAT* inside us by *increasing metabolism* (i.e. converting more energy).

Realistically Hairs Standing on End make No Difference to Humans

When you get *goosebumps* and your hairs *stand on end*, it isn't going to keep you any warmer because you have virtually no hair on your body. It's a leftover from when we had hairy bodies. However, *in your Exam* you'll dutifully mention it *to get the marks*.

These days we just put *more layers of clothes on*, to trap *more layers of air*.
This works really well because *trapped air acts as an insulator*. — *LEARN those details*.

So much to learn — don't let it get under your skin...

I can count about 15 important facts to learn on this page, plus a couple of suitably splendid diagrams. *Learn the headings* for each section, then *cover the page* and *scribble* out the details.

Revision Summary for Section Three

Section Three's got all sorts of grisly bits and bobs in it. And some of it can be really quite hard to understand too. But it's all worth points in the Exam, and what do points mean? Prizes! These questions are designed to test what you know. They're pretty tough I grant you, but they really are the best way of revising. Keep trying these questions any time you feel like it, and for any you can't do, look back in Section Three and learn the answer to it for next time.

1) Draw a diagram of the body and label the four places where hormones are produced. Give details of what each hormones does.
2) What is an endocrine gland? Give the proper definition of hormones.
3) Give four details to compare nerves with hormones.
4) Explain what happens with insulin when the blood sugar is too high and when it is too low.
5) Draw diagrams to illustrate exactly what goes on in both cases.
6) What happens in diabetes? What are the two forms of treatment? How do they compare?
7) Give full details of the four stages in the female menstrual cycle.
8) Sketch the single diagram showing the state of the uterus lining at each stage.
9) What are the two main hormones involved in the female menstrual cycle?
10) Sketch the diagram showing the uterus lining, along with the graph showing the levels of both hormones over the 28 days. Say which hormone causes each part of the cycle.
11) Give a few details of how hormones are used to promote fertility.
12) Which hormone is used in "The Pill" and how does it work?
13) What are the two types of microbe? How big are they compared to a human cell?
14) How exactly do bacteria make you feel ill? Sketch three common bacteria.
15) What do viruses do inside you to reproduce? Illustrate with sketches.
16) What are the five ways that microbes can enter our bodies?
17) Give details of the defences we have against these five methods of entry.
18) What is meant by your "immune system"? What is the most important part of it?
19) List the three ways that white blood cells deal with invading microbes.
20) Draw diagrams to illustrate two of these lines of attack.
21) What are antibiotics? What will they work on and what will they not work on?
22) What are the two types of addiction to drugs.
23) List the five different types of "drug" with examples of each. List the dangers of each type.
24) Explain the dangers of drinking alcohol.
25) Explain why smoking is just *so cool — not.*
26) List in detail all five major health problems that result from smoking?
27) What is the proper definition for homeostasis?
28) What are the six bodily levels that are involved in homeostasis?
29) What are the three main things that the skin does for you?
30) Draw a diagram of the body showing the eight organs involved in homeostasis.
31) Say exactly what each of these organs does to help.
32) What is the basic function of the kidneys?
33) What *three* particular things do kidneys deal with?
34) What is urea? Where does it come from? Where does it go in the end?
35) Explain in detail exactly what the kidney does with ions in the blood, such as salt.
36) What three things are involved in the balance of water in our bodies?
37) What are the two treatments for kidney failure? Give the pros and cons of both.
38) What temperature do our bodily enzymes like?
39) Draw diagrams showing the three things the skin does when we're a) too hot b) too cold.
40) What else do our bodies do to keep warm? What else do *we* do to keep warm?

Types of Creature

There are SEVEN main classes of animals that you need to know about. Learn them:

Insects

INSECTS have:

1) A three-part body
2) Six legs
3) Two pairs of wings
4) One pair of antennae.

Spiders

SPIDERS have:

1) A two-part body
2) Eight legs
3) No wings.

Fish

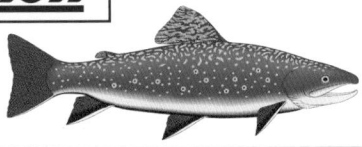

FISH have:

1) Slimy, bony scales
2) Gills
3) Fins
4) Thousands of eggs
5) No worries (about their young).

Amphibians

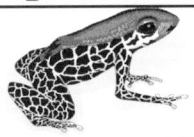

AMPHIBIANS have:

1) Slimy skin
2) Fish tails when young
   Four legs when adult
3) Hundreds of eggs
4) No worries (about their young).

Reptiles

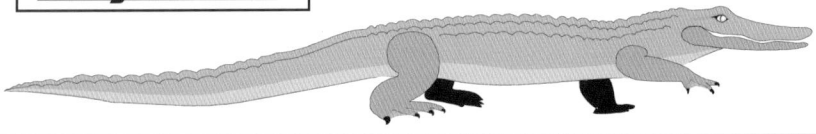

REPTILES have:

1) Dry leathery scales
2) Very small brains
3) Several dozen eggs
4) Few worries (about their young).

Birds

BIRDS have:

1) Dry feathers
2) Two legs and two wings
3) A dozen or so eggs
4) No teeth (beak instead)
5) Worries about eggs and young.

Mammals

MAMMALS have:

1) Dry hair
2) Four limbs
3) Don't lay eggs
4) Milk provided for youngsters
5) Worries over young — you bet.

Creature Features — learn them real good...

This is all quite nice easy stuff but make sure you know all the tricky details. In the Exams they could easily ask you to give, say, three differences between birds and bees. Make sure you know all about it before you get there. Learn it, then cover the page and scribble it all down.

Using a Key To Identify Creatures

A fairly easy type of question which they might give you, is to distinguish between several creatures using A KEY. A key is made up of questions with two possible answers.

You Have to Follow this Careful Method:

1) Take each creature, one at a time, and work through the questions carefully and slowly.
2) Follow the instructions for whichever answers are right for the chosen creature.
3) Eventually you reach an end where it says "Creature A:" or something like that.
4) Fill in the name of the creature you were doing. Easy as that. But always do it slowly.

Try it with this set of creatures using the KEY that follows:

Dung Beetle

Fish

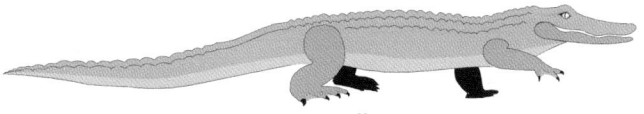
Alligator

Horse

Spider

Bird

VW

1) Soft exterior..... go to 2
   Hard exterior..... go to 5

2) Scales on exterior..... go to 3
   No scales on exterior..... go to 4

3) No legs ..... Creature A: .....FISH.....
   Four Legs ..... Creature B: .....

4) Four legs ..... Creature C: .....
   Not four legs ..... Creature D: .....

5) No wings..... Creature E: .....
   Two sets of Wings..... Beetle, go to 6

6) Six legs..... Creature F: .....
   Two doors..... Creature G: .....

Learn how to use Keys — or get caught out...

Remember, there's a wrong way and a right way to do this.
Do it the right way: Choose one creature at a time and go through the questions for just that one till you get an answer for it. Then do the next creature. Don't try to read a question first and then look for a creature that fits the bill — it all goes horribly wrong if you do that!

Answers

Creature A: Fish
Creature B: Alligator
Creature C: Horse
Creature D: Bird
Creature E: Spider
Creature F: Dung Beetle
Creature G: VW Beetle

Variation in Plants and Animals

The word "*VARIATION*" sounds far too fancy for its own good.
All it means is how animals or plants of the same species *look or behave slightly different from each other*. You know, a bit *taller* or a bit *fatter* or a bit more *scary-to-look-at* etc.
There are *two* causes of variation: *Genetic Variation* and *Environmental Variation*. Read on, and learn...

1) Genetic variation

You'll know this already. *All animals* (including humans) are bound to be *slightly different* from each other because their *GENES* are slightly different. Genes are the code inside all your cells which determine how your body turns out. We all end up with a slightly different set of genes.

The *exceptions* to that rule are *identical twins*, because their genes are *exactly the same*.
But even identical twins are never *completely identical* — and that's because of the other factor:

2) Environmental Variation is shown up by Twins

If you're not sure what "*environment*" means, think of it as "*upbringing*" instead — it's pretty much the same thing — how and where you were "brought up".

> Since we know the *twins' genes* are *identical*, any differences between them *must* be caused by slight differences *in their environment* throughout their lives.

Nice one Pauline!

Twins give us a fairly good idea of how important the *two factors* (genes and environment) are, *compared to each other*, at least for animals — plants always show *much greater variation* due to differences in their environment than animals do, as explained below.

Environmental Variation in Plants is much Greater

PLANTS are *strongly affected* by:
1) *Temperature* 2) *Sunlight* 3) *Moisture level* 4) *Soil composition*
For example, plants may grow *twice as big* or *twice as fast* due to *fairly modest* changes in environment such as the amount of *sunlight* or *rainfall* they're getting, or how *warm* it is or what the *soil* is like.

(A cat, on the other hand, born and bred in say, the North of Scotland, could be sent out to live in equatorial Africa and would show no significant changes — it would look the same, eat the same, and probably still puke up everywhere.)

To Test for the Effects of Environment on Plants

In many types of plant it's possible to produce *clones*, which are *genetically identical* to one another, just like twins are.

You can then expose such plants to various conditions to see how it affects them, knowing that *any differences in appearance* are due entirely to *environment*.

With *ordinary plants* (which are *NOT* clones) you have to do a bit of *experimenting* to test how much environment is affecting them. So plants make for tricky Exam questions:

> *"If two similar plants growing next to each other are different sizes, what's the reason for it — genetic variation or differences in environment?"*

The answer is that it could be either! To find out you'd need to carry out one of these two careful *TESTS*:

1) *PLANT TWO NEW PLANTS* of the *same species* in the *same positions* and see if the *same thing* happens. If the same place gives a smaller plant *again* you'd know the difference in size was *probably* due to differences in the environment between the two positions.
2) Or, you could plant *THE TWO ORIGINAL PLANTS* in *another place* and see if they start growing more alike. If they do, it suggests that differences in *environment* were the cause of the differences in growth.

Variation in Plants and Animals

Environmental Variation in Animals

Stubborn cats notwithstanding...
In Exams they do like questions on *the effects of environment on animals*.

Typically, they'll ask you *which features* of a human or a pet *MIGHT be affected* by their environment (i.e. the way they were "brought up").

In fact, *almost every single aspect* of a human (or animal) will be affected by *upbringing* in some way, however small, and in fact it's considerably easier to list the very few factors that *aren't* affected by environment:

4 Animal Characteristics NOT affected at all by Environment:

1) *EYE COLOUR*
2) *HAIR COLOUR* in most animals, (but not humans where vanity plays a big part)
3) *INHERITED DISEASES* like haemophilia, cystic fibrosis, etc.
4) *BLOOD GROUP*

And that's about it! So *learn those four* in case they ask you.

EVERYTHING ELSE is determined by *A MIXTURE* of *genetic* and *environmental* factors:
Body weight, *height*, *skin colour*, *condition of teeth*, *academic or athletic prowess*, etc. etc.

The *tricky* bit is working out just *how significant* environmental factors are for all these other features.
For example, imagine you got mixed up with another baby at the hospital and had grown up in a totally different household from your own. How different would you be now? It's not at all easy to tell how much of your physique and (more importantly) your personality are due to genes and how much to upbringing (environment). It's a big social issue, so it is.

Continuous and Discontinuous Variation:

CONTINUOUS VARIATION: The feature can vary over a *continuous range of values*.

Continuous variation refers to things like *height* or *weight* or *skin colour*, where the thing can have *any value at all* (within reason).
For example, the weight of a dog could be *absolutely anything* between say 2kg and 60kg: 5.3kg, 24.2kg, 24.23kg, 24.233kg, 35.1kg etc.

DISCONTINUOUS VARIATION: The feature can only take *one of several options*.

Discontinuous variation is things like *eye colour* or *blood group*, where there are just *a few definite options*, not a whole continuous range of possibles.
For example, eyes can only be *blue or brown or green or hazel*. They cannot be bluey-brown or kinda-greeney-bluey, or sorta-browney-bluey-kinda-hazeley, etc.

Two other examples are *DISEASE RESISTANCE IN LEAVES* and *LEAF AREA*. One shows *continuous* variation and the other shows *discontinuous* variation. You work out which is which.

Don't let Everything get to you — just learn the facts...

There are six sections on these two pages. After you think you've learnt it all, *cover the pages* and do a "*mini-essay*" on each of the six sections. Then *check back* and see what important points you missed. The coloured ink highlights the important bits — the rest is idle creative genius.

Human Reproduction

You need to know the names of all the parts and what they do.

The Female Reproductive Organs

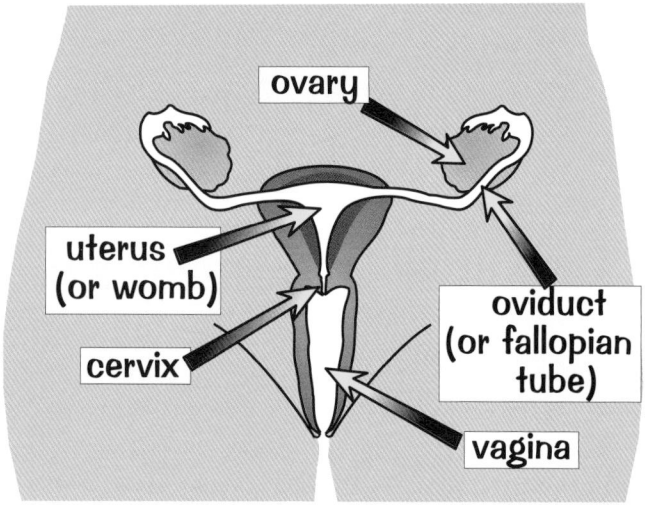

1) The *UTERUS* (or womb) is where the baby grows.

2) The *OVARIES* produce *eggs*, one every month. They also produce the *hormones* which control the *menstrual cycle*.

3) The *OVIDUCT* is what the eggs travel down to get to the womb. If the egg gets *fertilised* on its way down it will then *attach to the lining* of the uterus and grow into a *foetus*.

4) The *CERVIX* is just the entrance to the womb.

The Menstrual Cycle Takes Place Once a Month

This cycle of events takes place once every month.
The whole purpose of it is to prepare the womb for accepting a fertilised egg.
Full details are on P. 42 and P. 43, but this is basically what happens:

1) The female body *prepares the womb-lining* to receive a fertilised egg (should there be one), and *an egg is released* from one of the ovaries.

2) If the egg *isn't* fertilised, the uterus lining *breaks down* and results in "bleeding" for several days, before the cycle starts again.

The Male Reproductive Organs

1) The *SPERM* are made in the *testes*.

2) The *prostate gland* and *seminal vesicle* make a fluid for the sperm to swim in which contains "energy" for them. This fluid is mixed with the sperm as they pass by. The final mixture of sperm and fluid is called *semen*.

3) Under certain "circumstances" the semen passes out through the *urethra*.

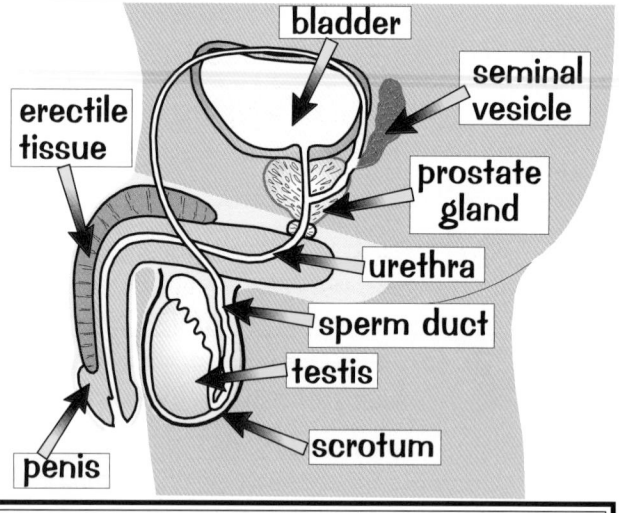

Let's see how much you can reproduce then...

YOU KNOW THE DRILL. Learn the information, then turn over and scribble down what you can remember. You'll find there are always some bits that are harder to learn than others. That's why this method of revision is so perfect — it concentrates your effort *just where it's needed*.

Fertilisation and The Embryo

Fertilisation

1) Sperm are deposited in the vagina by an obliging male and they swim up through the cervix and into the oviducts.

2) Millions of sperm are deposited but only a few hundred reach the egg. The rest die.

3) Fertilisation needs to takes place quite high up in the oviduct, because the egg only survives for about a day.

Sperm are tiny, don't forget, not like those gurt "tadpoles" in the diagram

4) When the sperm reach the egg, they cluster round it and eventually one of them gets through the egg membrane.

5) The egg membrane instantly changes to prevent any more sperm getting in.

6) When the nucleus of the successful sperm fuses with the nucleus of the egg, fertilisation has taken place. A zygote has then been produced.

7) If it gets fertilised, the zygote divides (by mitosis) and soon becomes a veritable ball of cells.

8) After about seven days, the ball of cells reaches the uterus, where it implants itself into the lining. This process is called implantation, oddly enough. The ball of cells is now called an EMBRYO.

NON-IDENTICAL twins occur if two different eggs get fertilised, perhaps one from each ovary. IDENTICAL twins form if the new ball of cells somehow splits in two at an early stage — both halves then grow into full embryos.

The Embryo

The ball of cells continues to divide and multiply. When all the organs have developed it's called a foetus. This takes about 11 weeks.

THE PLACENTA acts as a big exchange surface between the mother and baby, with blood capillaries filling it from both sides.

FOOD AND OXYGEN diffuse across from the mother's blood and WASTES are taken away by it.

Unfortunately, HARMFUL SUBSTANCES can also pass from the mother, such as alcohol, bacteria, viruses and drugs, and carbon monoxide from cigarette smoking.

That's why pregnant women need to be very careful what they do. The growing embryo is VERY DELICATE and can easily be damaged by harmful things in the mother's blood.

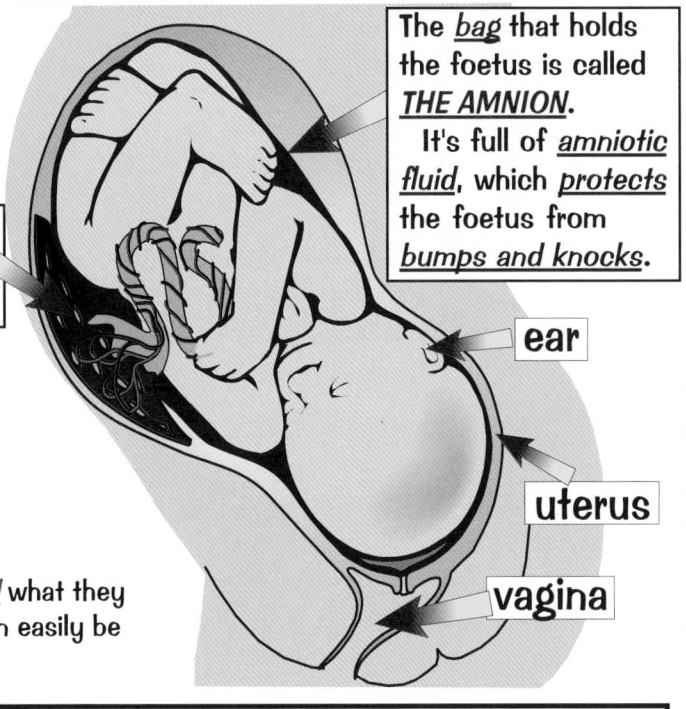

Well, my little spotty Zygote, have you learnt it all yet...

Follow the drill. But concentrate on the bits you DON'T know — NOT the bits you already do!

Genes, Chromosomes and DNA

You definitely need to learn these confusing words and exactly what they mean. *You have to make sure you know* exactly what and where *chromosomes* are, and what and where a *gene* is.

Learn What and Where Genes and Chromosomes are:

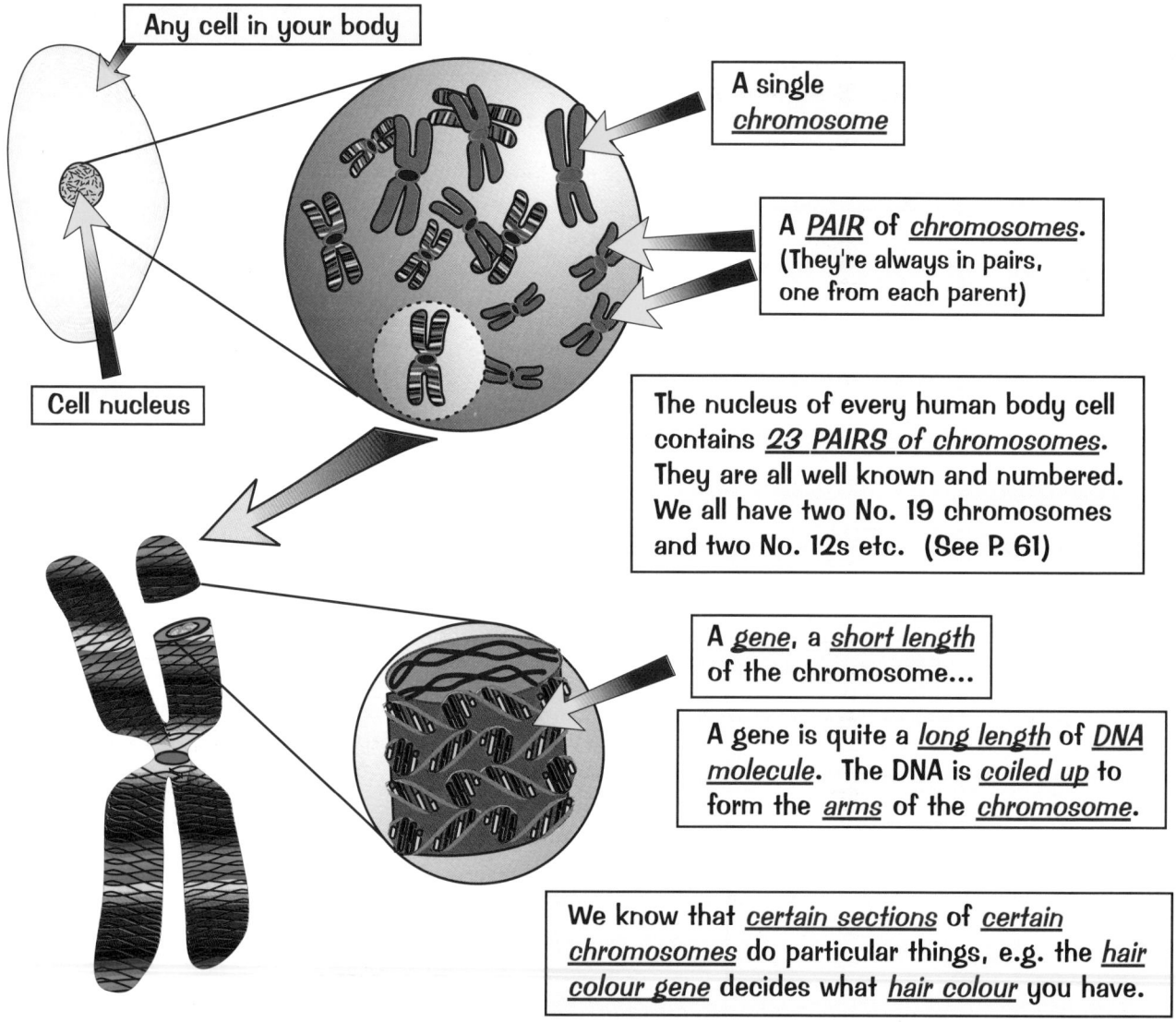

Genes are Chemical Instructions

1) *A gene is a length of DNA*.
2) So DNA is a long list of *instructions* on how to put the organism together and *make it work*.
3) Each *separate gene* is a separate *chemical instruction* to a particular type of cell.
4) An *ALLELE* is *another name for a gene*.
5) So sections of chromosome are also sometimes called *alleles*.
6) As a rule, you call them *alleles* instead of genes when you're talking about someone inheriting two *different* genes (alleles) from their parents — e.g. two different *alleles* for hair colour.

Hard Learning? — don't blow it all out of proportion...

This is a real easy page to learn, don't you think. Why, you could learn the whole thing with both ears tied behind your head. *Cover the page* and *scribble down* all the diagrams and details.

Fertilisation: Sperm and Egg Meet Up

There are 23 Pairs of Human Chromosomes

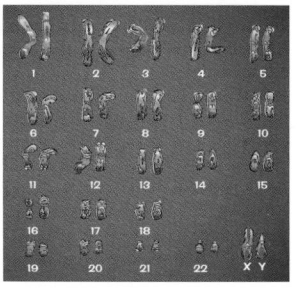

They are well known and numbered. In every cell nucleus we have two of each type. The diagram shows the 23 pairs of chromosomes from a human cell. One chromosome in each pair is inherited from each of our parents. Normal body cells have 46 chromosomes, in 23 pairs.

Remember, the two chromosomes in each pair are equivalent to each other. In other words, the number 19 chromosomes from both your parents pair off together, as do the number 17s etc. What you don't get is the number 12 chromosome from one parent pairing off with, say, the number 5 chromosome from the other.

Reproductive Cells Produce Sperm Cells or Egg Cells:

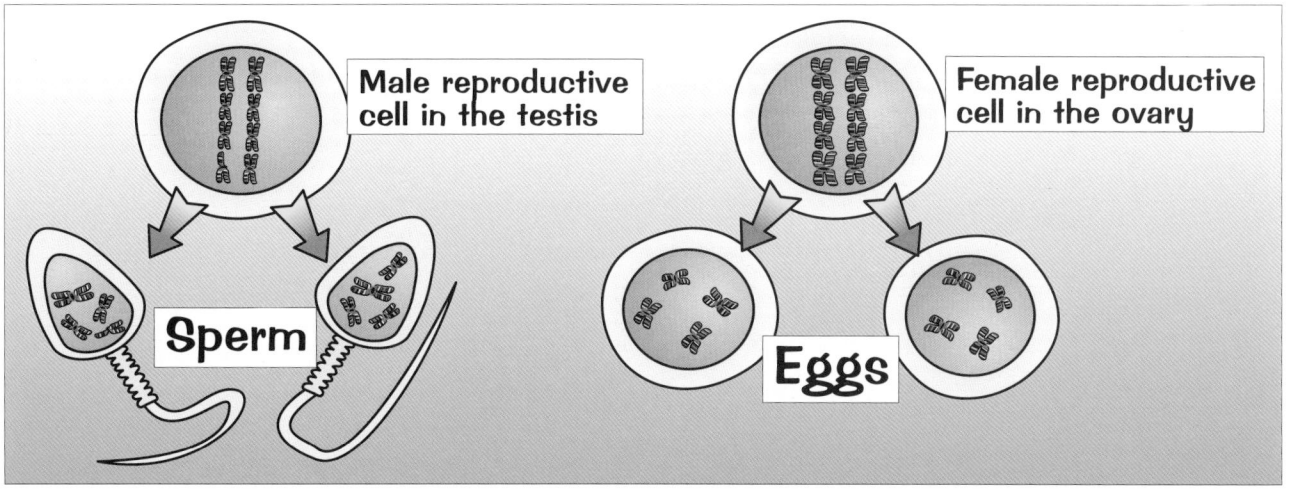

You will see that the sperm and egg only have one chromosome to describe each bit of you, one copy of each of the chromosomes numbered 1 to 23.
But a normal cell needs two chromosomes of each type — one from each parent, so...

Sperm and Egg Meet Up at Fertilisation:

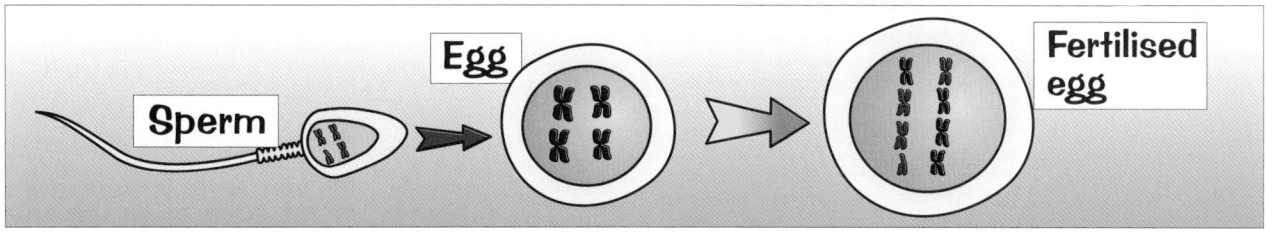

WHEN THE SPERM AND EGG MEET UP during fertilisation, the 23 single chromosomes in the sperm will all pair off with their appropriate "partner chromosomes" in the egg to form the full 23 pairs again: No. 4 with No. 4, No. 13 with No. 13, etc. etc.

Don't forget, the two chromosomes in a pair both contain the same basic genes, e.g. for hair colour, etc. When single chromosomes meet up at fertilisation, they seek out their "other half".

The resulting offspring will then receive its outward characteristics as a mixture from the two sets of chromosomes, so it will inherit features from both parents. Pretty cool, eh.

It should all be starting to come together now...

It's a bit tricky but you just need to get the gist that sperm and egg only have half the full number of chromosomes. When they meet up they combine to produce the full 46. Practise sketching out the sequence of diagrams, with the notes, till it all sinks in. Nice, innit.

Girl or Boy? — X and Y Chromosomes

There are 23 matched pairs of chromosomes in every human cell. You'll notice the 23rd pair is labelled XY. They're the two chromosomes that decide whether you turn out male or female. They're called the X and Y chromosomes because they look like an X and a Y.

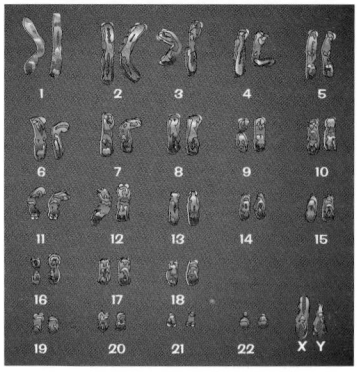

ALL MEN have *an X* and *a Y* chromosome: XY
The Y chromosome is DOMINANT and causes *male characteristics*.

ALL WOMEN have *two X chromosomes*: XX
The XX combination allows *female characteristics* to develop.

The diagram below shows the way the male XY chromosomes and female XX chromosomes *split up* to form the *eggs or sperm*, and then *combine together at fertilisation*.

The criss-cross lines show all the *possible* ways the X and Y chromosomes *could* combine. Remember, *only one of these* would actually happen for any offspring. What the diagram shows us is the ***RELATIVE PROBABILITY*** of each type of zygote (offspring) occurring.

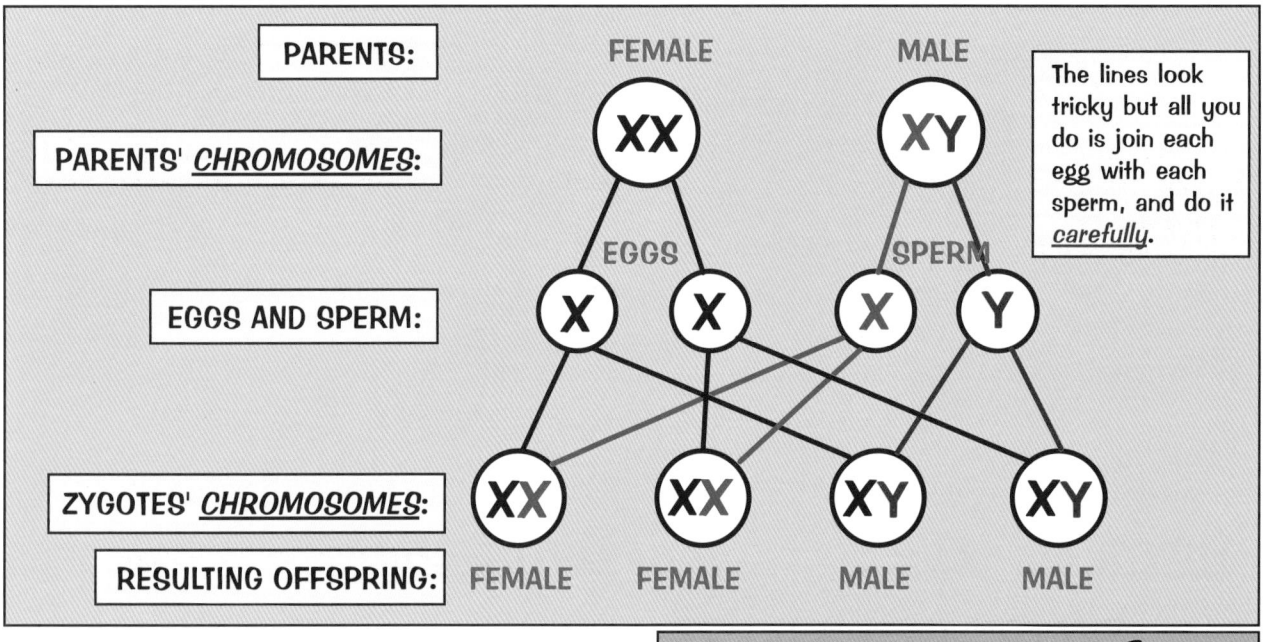

The other way of doing this is with a *checkerboard* type diagram. If you don't understand how it works, ask "Teach" to explain it. The *pairs of letters* in the middle show the possible offspring.

Both diagrams show that there'll be the *same proportion* of *male and female offspring*, because there are *two XX results* and *two XY results*.

Don't forget that this *50:50 ratio* is only a *probability*. If you had four kids they *could* all be *boys* — yes I know, terrifying isn't it.

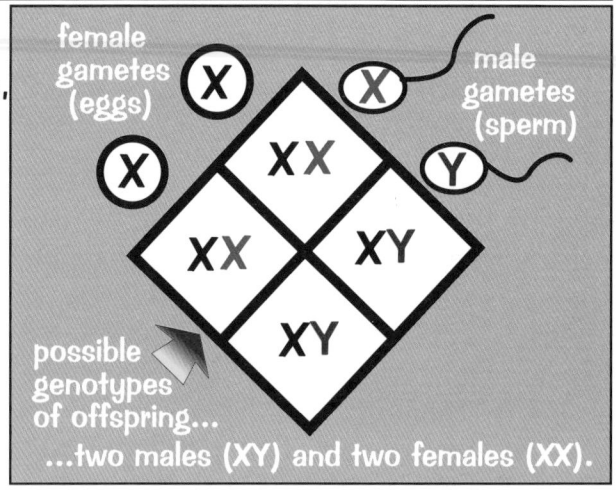

How can it take all that just to say it's a 50:50 chance...

Make sure you know all about X and Y chromosomes and who has what combination. The diagrams are real important. Practise reproducing them until you can do it *effortlessly*.

Clones and Asexual Reproduction

Learn this definition of clones:

CLONES are GENETICALLY IDENTICAL ORGANISMS

1) Clones occur naturally in both plants and animals. Identical twins are clones of each other.
2) These days clones are very much a part of the high-tech farming industry.
Hundreds of new plants can be produced very quickly from a single parent plant by taking cuttings from it. These bits of shoot or stem can be put into moist soil and will soon develop roots and grow into new plants.
This process is more successful with a) rooting compound and b) a very damp atmosphere.

In Asexual Reproduction There is Only One Parent

1) Ordinary cell division produces new cells identical to the original cell.
2) This is how all plants and animals grow. Their cells divide and multiply by replicating themselves.
3) However some organisms also reproduce this way — bacteria are a good example.
4) This is known as asexual reproduction. This is a DEFINITION of it, for you to learn:

In ASEXUAL REPRODUCTION there is only ONE parent, and the offspring therefore have EXACTLY THE SAME GENES as the parent — i.e. they're CLONES

Many Plants Reproduce Asexually — all by themselves

This means they produce exact genetic copies of themselves without involving another plant. Here are three common examples:

1) STRAWBERRY PLANTS producing *runners*,
2) New POTATO PLANTS growing from the tubers of old plants,
3) Bulbs such as DAFFODILS growing new bulbs off the side of them.

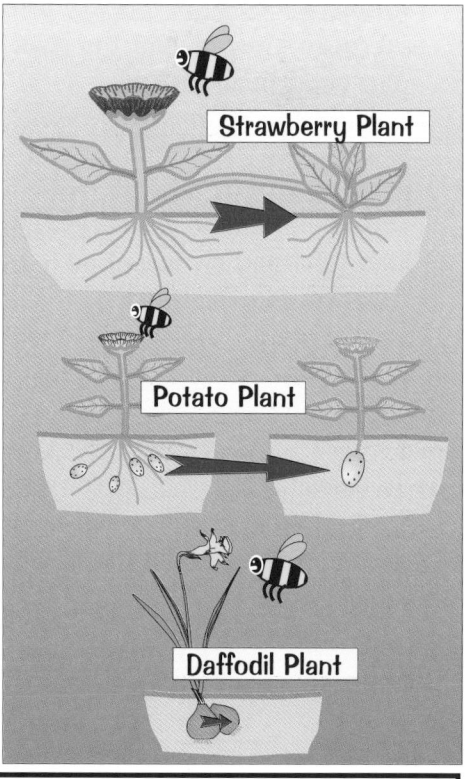

These Plants Must Also Reproduce Sexually

All of these plants also reproduce SEXUALLY — i.e. they attract insects to get cross-pollinated and hence produce genetically DIFFERENT offspring.

Strawberry, daffodil and potato plants produce flowers for this very purpose.

This is very important because cloning has the very serious drawback that there's no genetic variation amongst a population of clones so a change in environment, especially a new disease, could wipe the whole lot out. If a particular disease kills one of the clones, it will kill all the rest too. Not too good for the survival of the species, it has to be said.

Stop Cloning Around and just learn it...

I hope you realise that they could easily test your knowledge of any sentence on this page. I only put in stuff you need to know, you know. Practise scribbling out all the facts on this page, mini-essay style. Then cover the page and scribble it all down again. But most of all — smile.

Mutations

Mutations Show up as a Strange New Characteristic

1) A MUTATION occurs when an organism develops with some strange new characteristic that no other member of the species has had before.
2) For example if someone was born with blue hair it would be caused by a mutation.
3) Some mutations are beneficial, but most are disastrous (e.g. blue hair).

Mutations are Caused by Faults in Genes and Chromosomes

There are several ways that mutations happen, but in the end they're all down to faulty genes. Mutations usually happen when the chromosomes are replicating themselves and something goes wrong.

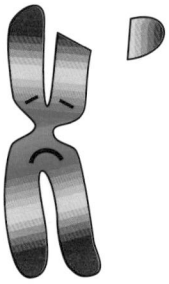

There are three ways of saying what a mutation is:

1) A mutation is a CHANGE TO A GENE or several genes.
2) A mutation is a CHANGE in one or more CHROMOSOMES.
3) A mutation STARTS IN THE NUCLEUS of one particular cell.

Radiation and Certain Chemicals cause Mutations

Mutations occur "naturally", probably caused by "natural" background radiation (from the sun and rocks etc.) or just the laws of chance that every now and then a chromosomes doesn't quite copy itself properly.
However the chance of mutation is increased by exposing yourself:

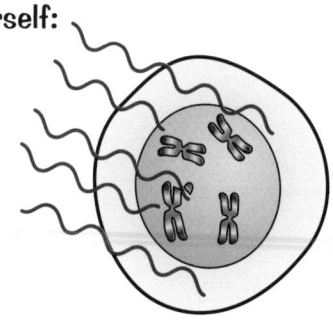

1) To nuclear radiation, i.e. alpha, beta and gamma radiation. This is sometimes called ionising radiation because it creates ions (charged particles) as it passes through stuff. (See the Physics Book.)
2) To X-rays and Ultra-Violet light, which are the highest-frequency parts of the EM spectrum (together with gamma rays).
3) To certain chemicals which are known to cause mutations. Such chemicals are called mutagens! If the mutations produce cancer then the chemicals are often called carcinogens.
4) Cigarette smoke contains chemical mutagens (or carcinogens)... (I'm sayin' nowt — See P. 47.)

Don't get your genes in a twist, this stuff's easy...

There are three sections with numbered points for each. Memorise the headings and learn the numbered points, then cover the page and scribble down everything you can remember.
I know it makes your head hurt, but every time you try to remember the stuff, the more it sinks in. It'll all be worth it in the end. Smile and enjoy.

Mutations

Most Mutations are Harmful

If a mutation occurs in reproductive cells, then the young may develop abnormally or die at an early stage of their development.

Mutations Often Cause Cancer

If a mutation occurs in body cells, the mutant cells may start to multiply in an uncontrolled way and invade other parts of the body. This is what we know as CANCER.

Some Mutations are Beneficial, giving us "EVOLUTION"

1) Blue "budgies" appeared suddenly as a mutation amongst yellow budgies. This is a good example of a neutral effect. It didn't harm its chances of survival and so it flourished (and at one stage, every grandma in Britain had one).

2) Very occasionally, a mutation will give the organism a survival advantage over its relatives, and it may well live on in conditions where the others die. This is natural selection and evolution at work.

3) A good example is a mutation in a bacteria that makes it resistant to antibiotics, so the mutant gene lives on, in the offspring, creating a resistant "strain" of bacteria, which antibiotics will not kill.
We then have to develop a new antibiotic to deal with the new resistant strain of bacteria. And so it goes on.

Down's Syndrome is Caused by Having Three No. 21s

1) This is a completely different type of genetic disease where a person ends up with THREE CHROMOSOME 21s in their cells.

2) Down's Syndrome is actually an example of a MUTATION. It is unlike most mutations which involve changes to genes. This one just involves having an EXTRA CHROMOSOME.

3) The problem happens in one of the woman's ovaries. Occasionally BOTH chromosome 21s go into the same egg cell, leaving the other with none. If the egg with two chromosome 21s is fertilised the resulting offspring will have THREE chromosome 21s.

4) This causes Down's Syndrome.

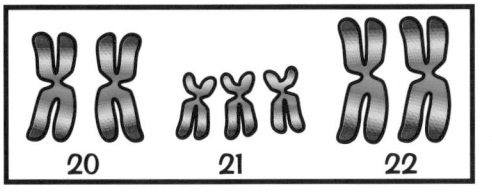

The main effects of Down's Syndrome are:

a) The child will have lower mental ability.
b) They are also generally more susceptible to certain diseases.
c) They tend to die quite young, around the age of thirty.

Learn the facts then see what you know...

There are three sections on this page, with several numbered points in each. You need to learn all these details about the harmful effects of mutations, including Down's Syndrome.
When you think you know it all, cover the page and scribble it all down again. Then check back and see what important points you missed. Remember, they could ask any of this stuff.

Cystic Fibrosis and Huntington's Chorea

Cystic Fibrosis — The Symptoms

1) CYSTIC FIBROSIS is a GENETIC DISEASE which affects about 1 in 1600 people in the UK.
2) It's caused by a defective gene on one of the chromosomes which the person inherits from their parents. There's still no cure or effective treatment for this condition.
3) The result of the defective gene is that the body produces a lot of thick sticky mucus in the lungs, which has to be removed by massage.
4) Excess mucus also occurs in the pancreas, causing digestive problems.
5) Much more seriously though, THE BLOCKAGE OF THE AIR PASSAGES in the lungs causes a lot of CHEST INFECTIONS.
6) Physiotherapy and antibiotics clear them up but slowly the sufferer becomes more and more ill.

Cystic Fibrosis must be Inherited from Both Parents

1) A person will only develop cystic fibrosis if they inherit the gene which causes it from both of their parents.
2) The parents must both be carriers of the defective gene which causes the disease, but neither of them will show the symptoms.
3) This is an important point about many genetic diseases — the parents are often carriers of the disorder, but without showing any symptoms at all.
4) If only one parent is a carrier, then the child will not develop this disease. The child could become a carrier though and pass on the problem to their own children one day.

There's Now a Test for the Cystic Fibrosis Gene, but...

1) It was only in 1989 that the gene causing cystic fibrosis was discovered.
2) Since then it has at least been possible to test parents to see if they are carriers.
3) Before that, the first indication was when a child was actually born with the disease.
4) If both parents find they are carriers, there's a difficult decision to be made about having kids, because each child they have has a one in four chance of developing the disease.

Huntington's Chorea is inherited From Just One Parent

1) UNLIKE cystic fibrosis (and sickle cell anaemia), this genetic disease is inherited if just one parent has the faulty gene.
2) If one parent does carry the faulty gene, there's a 50% CHANCE of any child developing the disease. THESE ARE SERIOUSLY GRIM ODDS.

Huntington's Chorea Causes Slow Deterioration of the Nervous System

1) The disease is not pleasant at all. It causes a steady collapse of the nervous system. This results in shaking, erratic body movements and severe mental deterioration.
2) The "carrier" parent will always become a sufferer too, but the symptoms do not appear until after the age of 40, by which time the faulty gene has been passed on to children and even grandchildren. Hence the disease keeps on going because sufferers always have plenty of time to reproduce before succumbing to the unpleasant symptoms.

Learn the facts then see what you know...

The symptoms are fairly easy to learn, but it's also important to learn the basic facts about how these two diseases are inherited, e.g. whether one or both parents need to be carriers and whether or not they'll show symptoms. Learn it all, then cover the page and scribble it out.

Sickle Cell Anaemia and Haemophilia

Sickle Cell Anaemia — the Symptoms

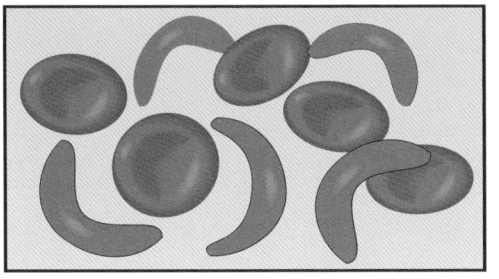

1) This disease causes the RED BLOOD CELLS to be shaped like SICKLES instead of the normal round shape.
2) They then get stuck in the capillaries which deprives body cells of oxygen.
3) It's an unpleasant, painful disease and sufferers die at an early age.

Like Cystic Fibrosis — it must be Inherited from Both Parents

1) The genetics are identical to cystic fibrosis. To inherit the disease both the parents must be carriers. Neither of them will show any symptoms though. The fancy way of saying this is that they are "symptomless carriers".
2) Yet even though sufferers die before they can reproduce, the occurrence of sickle cell anaemia doesn't always die out as you'd expect it to, especially not in Africa.
3) This is because carriers of the disease also turn out to be MORE IMMUNE TO MALARIA.
4) Hence, being a carrier of sickle cell anaemia actually increases the overall chance of a persons survival (in some parts of the world), even though some of their offspring are going to die young from sickle cell anaemia, which the parent will pass on to them.

Haemophilia — The Symptoms

1) The main symptom of haemophilia is that BLOOD DOES NOT CLOT properly.
2) This means that even small cuts and tooth extractions can be LETHAL, due to blood loss.
3) Small knocks can cause internal bleeding and big bruises, and joints may also bleed.
4) These days, however, the condition can be treated quite successfully by regular injections of the clotting factor, FACTOR 8.

Only Males get Haemophilia

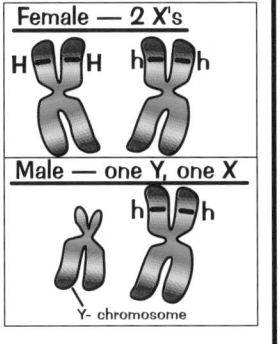

1) HAEMOPHILIA is only present in MALES.
2) This is because there's a defective gene on the X-chromosome.
3) A man inherits only one X-chromosome (and one Y-chromosome — that's what makes him male).
4) However, the Y-chromosome is SHORTER than the X-chromosome and so has quite a few genes MISSING.
5) So a faulty gene on the man's (one and only) X-chromosome will cause trouble because the equivalent gene (which *would* work properly) is missing on his Y-chromosome (see diagram).
6) The other feature of this disease is that although females never suffer the disease, they can still be carriers and pass it on to their sons.

Learn the facts then see what you know...

These diseases are all mentioned in the syllabuses and questions on them are very likely. You need to learn all this very basic information on them. Cover the page and scribble it all down.

Selective Breeding

Selective Breeding is Very Simple

SELECTIVE BREEDING is also called artificial selection. This is because humans artificially select the plants or animals that are going to breed and flourish, according to what WE want from them.

This is the Basic Process involved in Selective Breeding:

1) From your existing stock select the ones which have the BEST CHARACTERISTICS.
2) Breed them with each other.
3) Select the best of the OFFSPRING, and combine them with the best that you already have and breed again.
4) Continue this process over SEVERAL GENERATIONS to develop the desired traits.

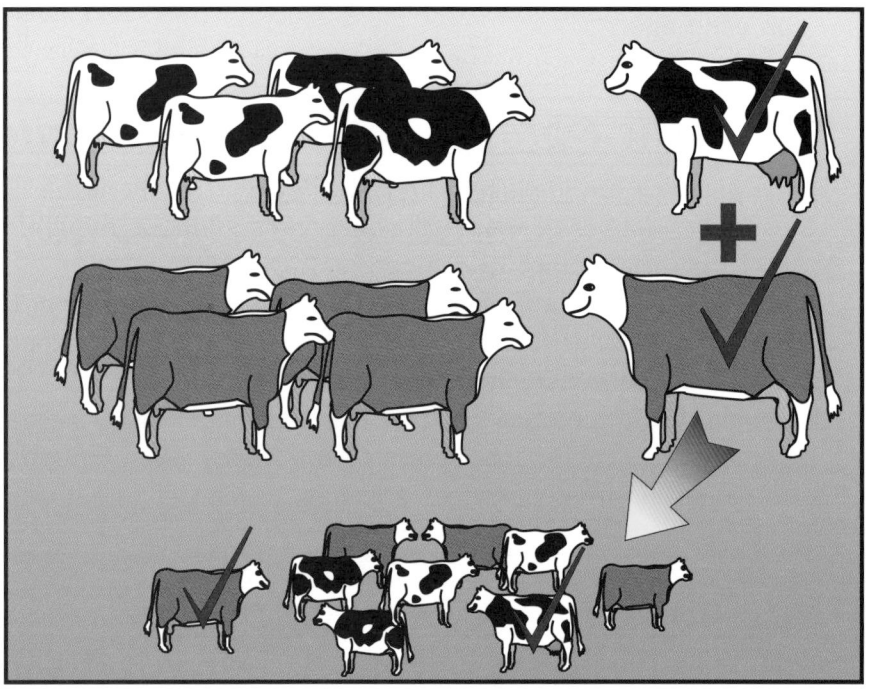

Selective Breeding is Very Useful in Farming

Artificial Selection like this is used in most areas of modern farming, to great benefit:

Selective Breeding Produces Better Sheep, Cows, Pigs, Chickens, etc.

1) Selectively breeding BEEF CATTLE to get the best beef (taste, texture, appearance, etc).
2) Selectively breeding MILKING COWS to increase milk yield and resistance to disease.
3) Selectively breeding CHICKENS to improve egg size and number of eggs per hen.

Selective Breeding Produces Better Wheat, Flowers, etc.

4) Selectively breeding WHEAT to produce new varieties with better yields and better disease resistance too.
5) Selectively breeding FLOWERS to produce bigger and better and more colourful ones.

Don't sit there brooding over it, just learn the info...

Selective breeding is a very simple topic. In the Exam they'll likely give you half a page explaining how a farmer in Sussex did this or that with his crops or cows, and then they'll suddenly ask: "What is meant by selective breeding". That's when you just write down the four points at the top of the page. Then they'll ask you to "Suggest other ways that selective breeding might be used by farmers in Sussex to improve their yield". That's when you just list some of the five examples that you've learnt. Easy peasy. Learn and enjoy...

Selective Breeding

The Main Drawback is Vulnerability to New Diseases

In farming, animals are selectively bred to develop the best features, which are basically:

1) MAXIMUM YIELD of meat, milk, grain, etc.
2) GOOD HEALTH and DISEASE RESISTANCE.

1) Selective breeding on farms involves choosing the best specimens in your selection and breeding from them, and then breeding them with the best of their children. This results in a lot of inter-breeding which can start to cause various problems.
2) The most serious problem it creates is the danger of a new disease coming along and wiping out all the plants or animals — the whole lot in one go.
3) This is made more likely because all the stock are closely related to each other, so if one of them is going to be killed by a new disease, the others are also likely to succumb to it.

Selective Breeding in Dogs Produces Many New Breeds

1) Dogs are another really good example of selective breeding.
2) The original dogs were all pretty much like wolves, but once man started working with them, first of all for hunting and later for herding sheep etc., he soon learnt to breed only from the most useful dogs and so the many different breeds gradually developed, with some more suited to herding (e.g. collies), others to hunting (e.g. terriers), etc. etc.

Pedigree Dogs can Develop Health Problems

However, these two factors don't really apply to selective breeding in pedigree dogs where physical appearance is the only thing that seems to matter — purely for winning dog shows.

Many pedigree dogs (in fact most pedigree dogs) have quite bad health problems because of this artificial selection. They are selected for breeding only on the basis of how well they match the "official" specification.

Random Cross-Breeds can be Much Healthier Dogs

1) Mongrels (random cross-breeds) on the other hand, are usually much healthier, fitter dogs because they're not so interbred.
2) They're very often much nicer natured and they can be real pretty too.
3) The word "mongrel" does them no justice at all. If you want a really great dog, my advice is go to the dog rescue place and get a crazy cross-breed and just love him.

Learn the facts then see what you know...

Make sure you know what the big disadvantage with selective breeding can be. Also learn how it has produced all the different breeds of dogs that we have today. Also note the difference between dogs that are bred as working dogs on the basis of health and aptitude, and those that are bred for dog shows. Learn the whole page then cover it up and scribble it all down.

Fossils

FOSSILS are the "remains" of plants and animals which lived millions of years ago.

There are Three ways that Fossils can be Formed:

1) From the hard parts of animals.
2) From the softer parts of plants or animals.
3) When no decay happens at all.

1) Fossils Usually Form from the Hard Parts of Animals

(Most fossils happen this way)

1) It's usually the hardest parts of animals like bones, teeth, shells, etc. which eventually become fossils.
2) That's because these things don't decay easily, so they tend to last a long time when buried.
3) Eventually they're replaced by minerals as they decay, forming a rock-like substance shaped like the original hard part.
4) The surrounding sediments also turn to rock, but the fossil stays distinct inside the rock, and eventually someone digs it up.

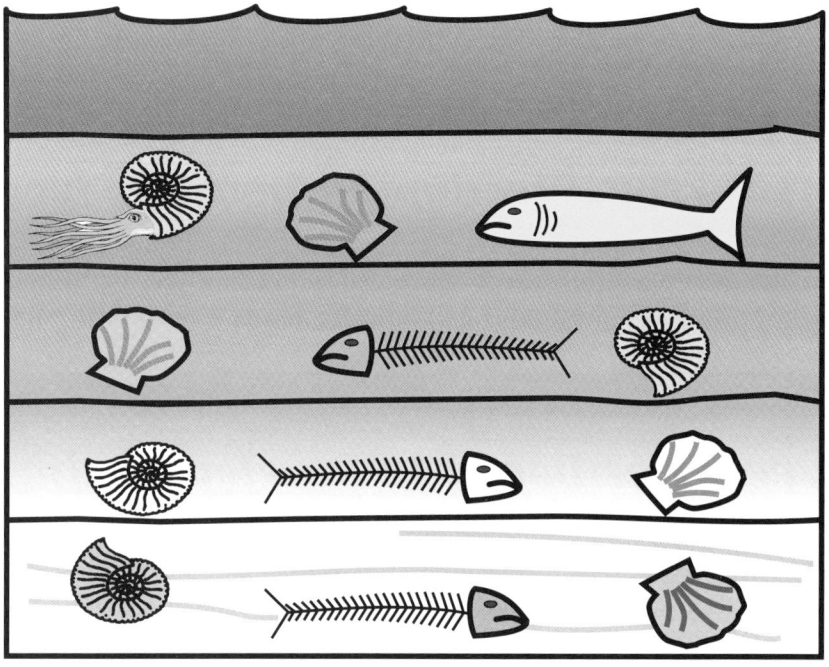

2) Petrification

— When Fossils Form from the Softer Parts of Animals or Plants

1) Sometimes fossils are formed from the softer parts which somehow haven't decayed.
2) The soft material gradually becomes "petrified" (turns to stone) as it slowly decays and is replaced by minerals.
3) This is rare, since there are very few occasions when decay occurs so slowly.
4) Most plant fossils are of this type because plants are generally soft and decay quickly.
5) For petrification to happen, the plant or animal usually has to fall into a swamp or bog and be covered quickly.
6) If there is virtually no oxygen reaching the plant it will not decay quickly, and petrification can gradually take place.

Fossils

3) In Places where No Decay Happens

When no decay whatsoever happens, then the *whole original plant or animal* may survive for *thousands of years*.

There are *THREE IMPORTANT EXAMPLES*:

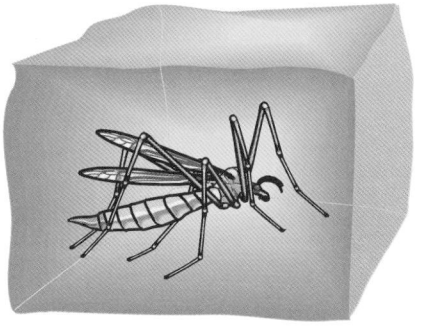

1) AMBER — no *OXYGEN* or *MOISTURE* for the *decay microbes*.

INSECTS are often found *fully preserved* in amber, which is a clear yellow "stone" made of *FOSSILISED RESIN* that ran out of an ancient tree hundreds of millions of years ago, engulfing the insect.

2) GLACIERS — too *COLD* for the *decay microbes* to work.

A *HAIRY MAMMOTH* was found fully preserved in a *glacier* somewhere several years ago.
(At least that's what I heard, though I never saw any pictures of it so maybe it was a hoax, I'm not really sure, but in principle one could turn up any time...)

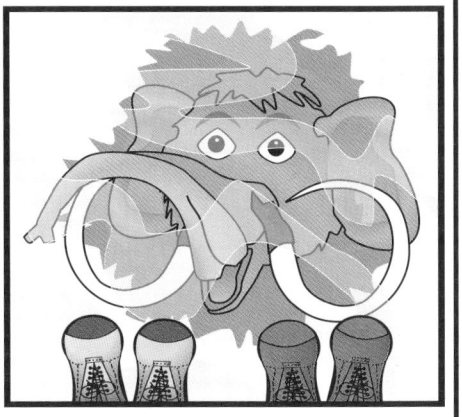

3) WATERLOGGED BOGS — too *ACIDIC* for *decay microbes*.

A *10,000 year old man* was found in a bog a few years ago. He was dead, and a bit squashed but otherwise quite well preserved, although it was clear he had been *murdered*.
(Police are not looking for any witnesses and have asked anyone *else* who thinks they may have important information to just keep away.)

Evidence from Rock and Soil Strata

The fossils found in *rock layers* tell us *TWO THINGS*:

1) What the creatures and plants *LOOKED LIKE*.
2) *HOW LONG AGO THEY EXISTED*, by the type of rock they're in.

Generally speaking, the *DEEPER* you find the fossil, the *OLDER* it will be, though of course rocks get pushed upwards and eroded, so very old rocks can become exposed.

Fossils are usually *dated* by geologists who *ALREADY KNOW THE AGE OF THE ROCK*.

The *Grand Canyon* in Arizona is about *1 mile deep*. It was formed by a river slowly cutting down through layers of rock. The rocks at the bottom are about *1,000,000,000 years old*, and the fossil record in the sides is pretty cool.

Don't get bogged down in all this information...

Make sure you're fully aware of the *three* different types of *fossil* and how they're *formed*.
Also make sure you learn all the details about what information rocks provide.
Many people read stuff and then think they know it.
It's only when you *cover it up* that you find out what you *really* know.

Evolution

The Theory of Evolution is Cool

1) This suggests that all the animals and plants on Earth gradually "*evolved*" over *millions of years*, rather than just suddenly popping into existence. Makes sense.
2) Life on Earth began as *simple organisms living in water* and gradually everything else evolved from there. And it only took about *3,000,000,000 years*.

Fossils Provide Evidence for Evolution

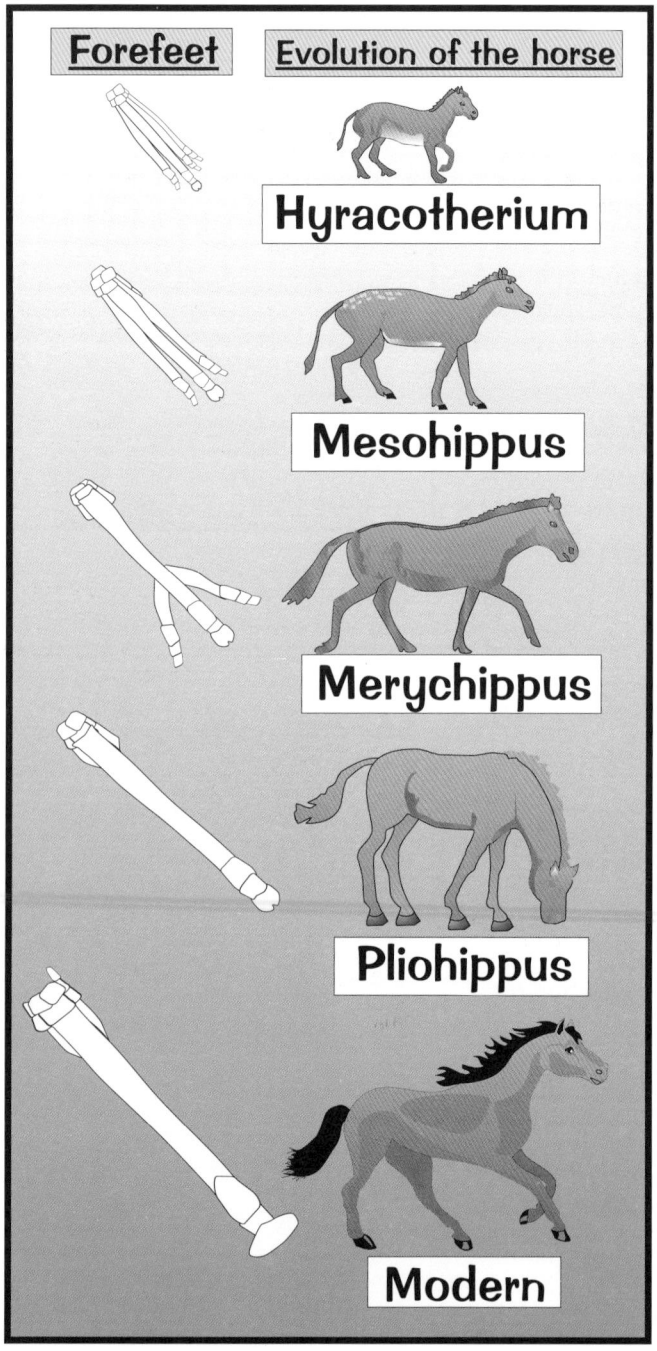

1) *Fossils* provide lots of *evidence* for evolution.
2) They show how today's species have *changed and developed* over *millions of years*.
3) There are quite a few "*missing links*" though because the fossil record is *incomplete*.
4) This is because *very very few* dead plants or animals actually turn into fossils.
5) Most just *decay away* completely.

The Evolution of The Horse is Ace

1) One set of fossils which *is* pretty good though is that showing *the evolution of the horse*.
2) This developed from quite a small creature about the size of a *dog* and the fossils show how the *middle toe* slowly became bigger and bigger and eventually evolved into the familiar *hoof* of today's horse.
3) It took about *60 million years* though.
4) This is *pretty strong evidence* in support of *evolution* because it really shows evolution happening.

Stop horsing around and just learn the facts...

You need to remember exactly what the theory of evolution is, because they could ask you. You also need to remember that fossils provide strong evidence in support of evolution theory. The fossil record of the horse is especially complete and convincing. *Learn and scribble*...

Extinction

Extinction is Pretty Bad News

It's only Fossils that tell us they Ever Existed at all

1) The *dinosaurs* and *hairy mammoths* became ***EXTINCT*** . That means they were totally wiped out.
2) It's only ***FOSSILS*** that tell us they ever existed at all (and the odd questionable glacier story).
3) There are *many thousands* of other plant and animal species which have come and gone too.

There are ***THREE WAYS*** a species can become ***EXTINCT***:

1) The ***ENVIRONMENT CHANGES*** too quickly.
2) A ***NEW PREDATOR*** or ***DISEASE*** kills them all.
3) They can't ***COMPETE*** with another (new) species for ***FOOD***.

Extinction Happens When the Environment Changes Too Fast

1) As the environment *slowly changes*, it will gradually favour certain new characteristics amongst the members of the species and over many generations those features will *proliferate*.
2) In this way, all species *constantly adapt* to their changing environment.
3) But if the environment changes *too fast* a whole species may be *wiped out*, i.e. *extinction*...

The Dinosaurs Were Probably Blatted by a big Meteorite

1) A *likely cause* for the *demise* of the dinosaurs was a *large meteorite* hitting the Earth. Such an impact would throw *millions of tonnes* of dust into the atmosphere.
2) This would *block out* the sun's rays and *totally alter the climate* all over the globe, literally overnight. It'd make it very cold.
3) Many species would be *unable to adapt* to such a *sudden and drastic change* in their environment and would *die out* very quickly. The *dinosaurs* were one of them.
4) But our ancestors *survived* and here we are today, just 60 million years later, working it all out.

Don't roll over and die — just learn the facts...

Another stupefyingly easy page to learn. Use the *mini-essay* method. Just make sure you *learn every fact*, that's all. Dinosaurs never did proper revision and look what happened to them. (Mind you they did last about 200 million years, which is about 199.9 million more than we have, so far...)

Revision Summary for Section Four

Gee, all that business about genes and chromosomes and the like — it's all pretty serious stuff, don't you think? It takes a real effort to get your head round it all. There's too many big fancy words, for one thing. But there you go — life's tough and you've just gotta face up to it. Use these questions to find out what you know — and what you don't. Then look back and learn the bits you didn't know. Then try the questions again, and again...

1) List the seven classes of animal and give three characteristics of each type.
2) Sketch an example of each of the seven types of animal.
3) What is the right method for using a KEY to identify creatures?
4) What are the two types of variation? Which type of variation is shown up by twins?
5) Does environment affect plants more than animals?
6) List four features of animals which aren't affected at all by environment, and four which are.
7) What is meant by continuous and discontinuous variation? Give two examples of each.
8) Draw a diagram of the main parts of the female reproductive system.
9) Draw a diagram of the main parts of the male reproductive system.
10) For both of the above, describe what each bit does.
11) What is the female menstrual cycle for?
12) Draw a sequence of diagrams showing how sperm reach the egg and fertilise it.
13) Also describe what happens to the fertilised egg as it travels on down to the uterus.
14) What is implantation? What is the difference between a zygote, an embryo and a foetus?
15) Sketch a foetus in the womb. Show the amnion and placenta and explain what they do.
16) Draw a set of diagrams showing all these things: cell, nucleus, chromosomes, genes, DNA.
17) Genes are chemical instructions. What instructions do they give?
18) How many pairs of chromosomes are there in a normal human cell nucleus?
19) What happens to the chromosome numbers when eggs and sperm are made?
20) What happens to the chromosome numbers during fertilisation?
21) What are X and Y chromosomes to do with? Who has what combination?
22) Draw a genetic inheritance diagram to show how X and Y chromosomes are passed on.
23) Explain how this gives an equal proportion of boys and girls.
24) What are clones? Give a common example of clones. How are plants cloned?
25) What is asexual reproduction? Give a proper definition for it.
26) Name three plants that reproduce asexually. Explain how they also reproduce sexually.
27) Give three definitions of what a mutation is. List the four main causes of mutations.
28) Give an example of a) harmful, b) neutral, and c) beneficial mutations.
29) What are the symptoms of Down's Syndrome? Explain why it is a mutation.
30) List the symptoms and treatment of cystic fibrosis. What causes this disease?
31) What test results will mean that a child is likely to be born with cystic fibrosis?
32) Give the symptoms of Huntington's Chorea? How is this disease caused?
33) When is a child likely to develop Huntington's Chorea?
34) Give the cause and symptoms of sickle cell anaemia. Why does it not die out?
35) What are the symptoms and treatment of haemophilia?
36) What causes haemophilia? Do both males and females show the symptoms of haemophilia?
37) Describe the basic procedure in selective breeding (of cows). Give five other examples.
38) What is the main drawback of selective breeding in a) farming b) pedigree dogs?
39) Describe fully the three ways that fossils can form. Give examples of each type.
40) Explain how fossils found in rocks support the theory of evolution. Refer to the horse.
41) What is meant by extinction? What usually causes extinction?
42) What probably wiped out the dinosaurs? Have many other species become extinct?

Adapt and Survive

If you *learn the features* that make these animals well adapted, you'll be able to apply them to any other similar animal they might give you in the Exam. Chances are you'll get a *camel* or a *polar bear* anyway.

The Polar Bear — Designed for Arctic Conditions

The *Polar bear* has all these features: (which *many other arctic creatures* have too, so think on...)

1) *Large size* and *compact shape* (i.e. rounded), including dinky little ears, to keep the *surface area* to a *minimum* (compared to the body weight) — this all *reduces heat loss*.
2) A *thick layer of blubber* for *insulation* and also to survive hard times when *food is scarce*.
3) *Thick hairy coat* for keeping the body heat in.
4) *Greasy fur* which *sheds water* after swimming to *prevent cooling* due to evaporation.
5) *White fur* to match the surroundings for *camouflage*.
6) *Strong swimmer* to catch food in the water and *strong runner* to run down prey on land.
7) *Big feet* to *spread the weight* on snow and ice.

The Camel — Designed for Desert Conditions

The *camel* has all these features: (most of which are shared by *other desert creatures*...)

1) It can *store* and *lose* a lot of *water* without problem. It can drink up to *20 gallons* at once.
2) It *loses very little water*. There's *little urine* and *very little sweating*.
3) It can tolerate *big changes* in its own *body temperature* to remove need for sweating.
4) *Large feet* to *spread load* on soft sand.
5) All *fat* is stored in the *hump*, there is *no layer of body fat*. This helps it to *lose* body heat.
6) *Large surface area*. The shape of a camel is anything but compact, which gives it more surface area to *lose body heat* to its surroundings.
7) Its *sandy colour* gives good *camouflage*.

A Cactus is adapted to live in very Dry Conditions

1) *Small surface area* to reduce *water loss* — leaves are just *spines*.
2) *Stores water* in stem.
3) *Spines* with a *nasty taste*, or even *poisonous*, to deter *herbivores*.
4) Stomata *only open at night* to *reduce water loss* in day.
5) *Shallow spreading roots* to collect *maximum moisture*.

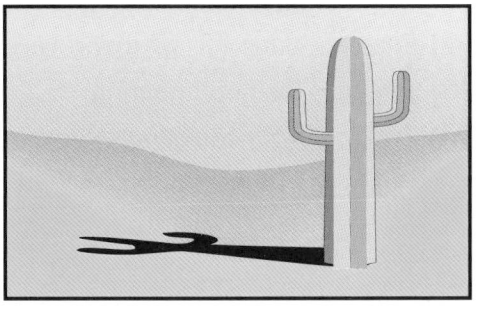

Creature features — learn and survive...

It's worth learning all these survival features well enough to be able to write them down *from memory*. These three are all specifically mentioned in the syllabuses. *Learn, cover, scribble*...

Prey and Predators

Populations of Prey and Predators go in Cycles

In a community containing prey and predators (as most of them do of course), the populations of the prey and predator tend to follow cycles of rise and fall. Learn why:

1) The POPULATION of any species is usually *limited* by the amount of FOOD available.
2) If the population of the PREY increases, then so will the population of the PREDATORS, because there's more food for them.
3) However as the population of predators INCREASES, the number of prey will DECREASE, because more of them will be getting eaten.
4) As the population of prey DECREASES, the population of PREDATORS will soon decrease AS WELL due to a shortage of food.
5) This *up and down pattern* continues, as shown on the graph...

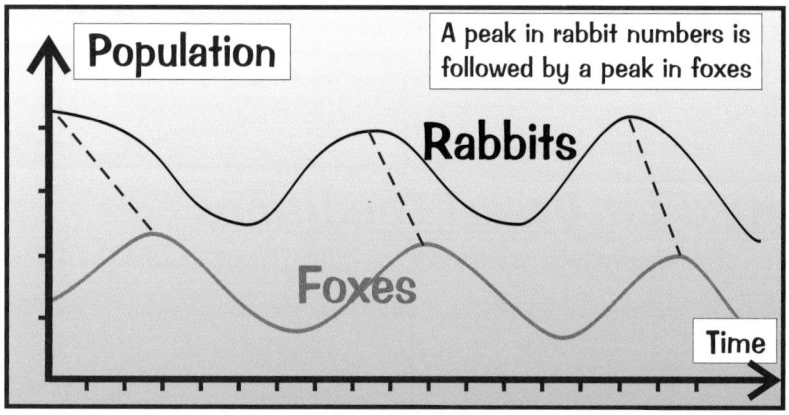

1) *More grass* means *more rabbits*.
2) More rabbits means *more foxes*.
3) But more foxes means *less rabbits*.
4) Eventually less rabbits will mean *less foxes again*.

The Lion — a perfect Predator

1) *Strong*, *agile* and *fast*.
2) *Strong jaws* and *sharp teeth* for killing prey.
3) Good *stereo vision* with both eyes *facing forwards*.
4) *Camouflaged body* for stalking prey.
5) The right sort of *teeth* for *chewing meat*.

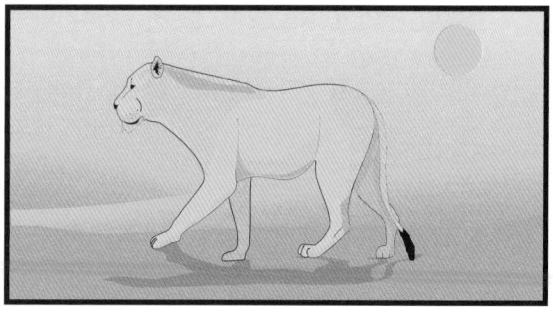

The Rabbit — a perfect Prey

1) *Fast* and *agile* for escaping capture.
2) Eyes on sides for *all-round vision*.
3) *Big ears* for good hearing.
4) *Brown colour* for *camouflage*.
5) *White tail* to alert pals.

Revision stress — don't let it eat you up...

There's a whole world full of animals and plants, all with different survival features, but explaining them eventually becomes kinda "*common sense*", because the same principles tend to apply to them all. Practise by thinking about different creatures and deciding what special features they have and why those features help them stay alive. Such jolly fun. *Learn and enjoy*.

Population Sizes

POPULATION SIZE just means how many of *one type of plant or animal* there is in a given ecosystem, and more importantly, WHY ONLY THAT MANY, why not more?

The answer is that there are always LIMITING FACTORS, such as *too little food* or *too many other animals* eating the food as well, or *too many animals eating them*, etc...

This can all start to get out of hand and sound really complicated.
But it's *really quite simple*, and you must keep telling yourself that!

Limits on Animal and Plant Populations

There are *two different ways* of looking at what affects the *size* of the population of any *species*:

Approach 1 — the size of the population of any animal or plant is due to SIX FACTORS:

1) The TOTAL AMOUNT OF FOOD or nutrients available.
2) The amount of COMPETITION there is (from other species) for the same food or nutrients.
3) The AMOUNT OF LIGHT AVAILABLE (this applies only to plants really).
4) The NUMBER OF PREDATORS (or grazers) who may eat the animal (or plant) in question.
5) DISEASE.
6) MIGRATION, i.e. some of the animals moving away to another place.

Approach 2 — the size of the population of any animal or plant is due to THREE FACTORS:

1) ADAPTATION — how well the animal has become *adapted to its environment*.
2) COMPETITION — how well the animal *competes with other species* for the same food.
3) PREDATION — how well the animal *avoids being eaten*.

In the Exam they could ask you about it from either of these two viewpoints.
Although these lists seem hard to relate to, what they're saying is surely just common sense...

In other words... organisms will thrive best if:

1) THERE'S PLENTY OF THE GOOD THINGS IN LIFE: food, water, space, shelter, light, etc.
2) THEY'RE BETTER THAN THE COMPETITION AT GETTING IT (better *adapted*).
3) THEY DON'T GET EATEN.
4) THEY DON'T GET ILL.

That's pretty much the long and the short of it, wouldn't you say? So learn those four things.
Every species is different, of course, but those FOUR basic principles will always apply.
In Exam questions YOU have to apply them to any new situation to work out what'll happen.

Brother! — it's a "dog eat dog" world alright...

It's a strange topic is population sizes. In a way it seems like it should be common sense, but it all seems to get so messy when you start trying to set it all down in an orderly way. Anyway, *learn all the points on this page* and you'll be OK with it, I'd think.

Atmospheric Pollution

The Three Main Sources of Atmospheric Pollution are...

1) Burning fossil fuels

1) Fossil fuels are coal, oil and natural gas.
2) The main culprits who burn these are cars and power stations.
3) They release mostly carbon dioxide, which is causing the greenhouse effect.
4) But they also release sulphur dioxide and oxides of nitrogen, which are causing acid rain.

2) CFCs (Chloro-fluoro-carbons)

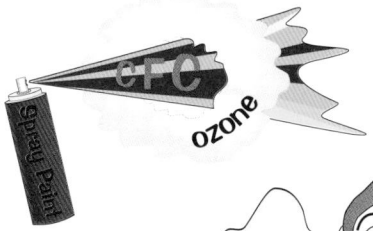

1) These are used in aerosols, fridges, air-conditioning units, and polystyrene foam.
2) They are causing a hole in the ozone layer.
3) This allows harmful UV rays to reach the Earth's surface.

3) Lead used in Petrol

1) "Old-fashioned" leaded (4 star) petrol contains lead which pollutes the air.
2) The lead is breathed in and causes damage to the nervous system.

People are usually OK at remembering the three sources of pollution in the atmosphere, but when it comes to sorting out their effects, it's a whole different ball game. You have to make a real effort to learn exactly where each type of pollution comes from and exactly what the effect of each pollutant is. For example, sulphur dioxide does not alter the Greenhouse Effect one squidget, and neither do CFCs. There are dozens of ways to get them all mixed up, but there are no marks for being a clot.

CFCs Cause The Hole in The Ozone Layer

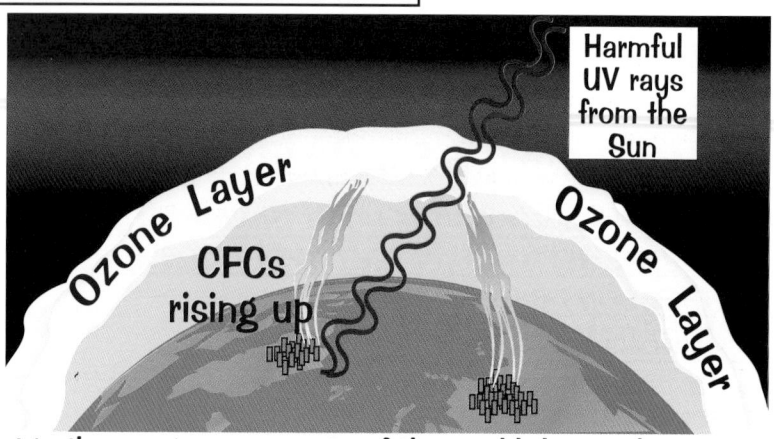

1) Ozone is molecules made of three oxygen atoms, O_3.
2) There is a layer of ozone high up in the atmosphere.
3) Ozone absorbs harmful UV rays from the Sun.
4) CFC gases react with ozone molecules and break them up.
5) This thinning of the ozone layer allows harmful UV rays to reach the surface of the Earth.
6) This is making it dangerous to go out in the sun in many parts of the world due to the increased risk of skin cancer from the harmful UV rays.
7) CFCs are being replaced by other gases now, but the harmful effects of the CFCs already released may continue for centuries.

Revision and Pollution — the two bugbears of modern life...

You must make a real effort to sort out the different types of air pollution. Notice for example that cars give out three different things which cause three different problems. Learn it good.

The Greenhouse Effect

Carbon Dioxide and Methane Trap Heat from the Sun

1) The *temperature* of the Earth is a *balance* between the heat it gets *from the Sun* and the heat it *radiates back out into space*.
2) The *atmosphere* acts like an *insulating layer* and keeps some of the heat *in*.
3) This is exactly what happens in a *greenhouse* or a *conservatory*.
   The sun shines *into it* and the glass *keeps the heat in* so it just gets *hotter and hotter*.
4) There are *several different gases* in the atmosphere which are very good at *keeping the heat in*. They are called "*greenhouse gases*", oddly enough. The *main ones* that we worry about are *methane* and *carbon dioxide*, because the levels of these are *rising quite sharply*.
5) The *Greenhouse Effect* is causing the Earth to *warm up* very slowly.

The Greenhouse Effect may cause Flooding and Drought ....(!)

1) *Changes* in *weather patterns* and *climate* could cause problems of *drought* or *flooding*.
2) The *melting* of the *polar ice-caps* would *raise sea-levels* and could cause *flooding* to many *low-lying coastal parts* of the world including *many major cities*.

Modern Industrial Life is Causing the Greenhouse Effect

1) The *level of CO_2* in the atmosphere used to be *nicely balanced* between the CO_2 *released by respiration* (of animals and plants) and the CO_2 *absorbed by photosynthesis*.
2) However, mankind has been burning *massive amounts* of *fossil fuels* in the last *two hundred years* or so.
3) We have also been *cutting down trees* all over the world to make space for living and farming. This is called *deforestation*.
4) The level of CO_2 in the atmosphere has *gone up* by about *20%*, and will *continue to rise* ever more steeply as long as we keep *burning fossil fuels* — just look at that graph — eek!

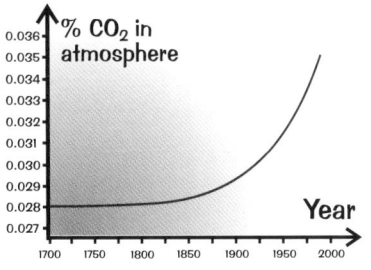

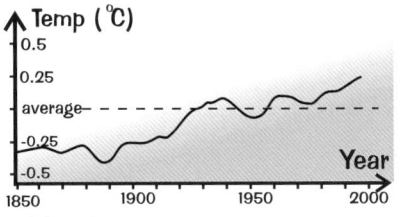

Methane is Also a Problem

1) *Methane gas* is also contributing to the *Greenhouse Effect*.
2) It's produced *naturally* from various sources, such as *natural marshland*.
3) However, the two sources of methane which are *on the increase* are:
   a) *Rice growing*
   b) *Cattle rearing* — it's the cows "pumping" that's the problem, believe it or not.

Learn the facts first — then start building your ark...

I bet you never realised there were so many drivelly details on the Greenhouse Effect.
Well there *are* and I'm afraid they could all come up in your Exam, so you just gotta learn them.
Use the good old *mini-essay* method for each section, and *scribble down what you know*...

Acid Rain

Burning Fossil Fuels Causes Acid Rain

1) When fossil fuels are burned they release mostly carbon dioxide which is causing the Greenhouse Effect. They also release two other harmful gases:
   a) SULPHUR DIOXIDE b) various NITROGEN OXIDES.
2) When these mix with clouds they form acids. This then falls as acid rain.
3) Cars and power stations are the main causes of acid rain.

Acid Rain Kills Fish, Trees and Statues

1) Acid rain causes lakes to become acidic which has a severe effect on its ecosystem.
2) The way this happens is that the acid causes aluminium salts to dissolve into the water. The resulting aluminium ions are poisonous to many fish and birds.
3) Acid rain kills trees.
4) Acid rain damages limestone buildings and ruins stone statues.

Acid Rain is Prevented by Cleaning up Emissions

1) Power stations now have acid gas scrubbers to take the harmful gases out before they release their fumes into the atmosphere.
2) Cars are now being fitted with catalytic converters to clean up their exhaust gases.
3) The other way of reducing acid rain is simply to reduce our usage of fossil fuels.

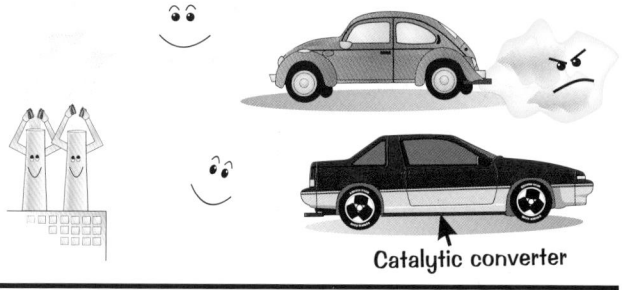

Learn about Acid Rain — and always take a coat...

There aren't too many details on acid rain. If you can't learn all this lot properly then you're just not trying. Don't forget they won't ask you easy stuff like "Is acid rain caused by cars or monkeys?", they'll test you on trickier stuff like "Which gases cause acid rain and why?". Learn and enjoy. And smile. ☺

There's Too Many People

The World Population is Rising Out of Control due to Modern Medicine and Agriculture

1) The population of the world is currently rising out of control as the graph shows.
2) This is mostly due to modern medicine which has stopped widespread death from disease.
3) It's also due to modern farming methods which can now provide the food needed for so many hungry mouths.

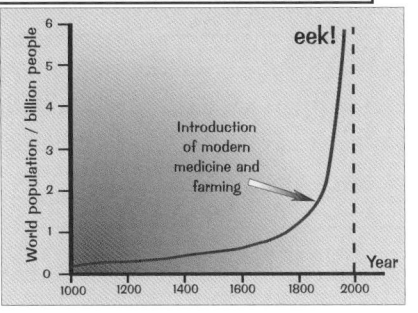

There's one born every minute — and it's too many

1) The death rate is now much lower than the birth rate in many under-developed countries. In other words there are lots more babies born than people dying.

2) This means the population must be rising.
3) In many poor countries it's rising very quickly.
4) This creates big problems for those countries trying to cope with all those extra people.
5) Even providing basic health care and education (about contraception!) is difficult, never mind finding them places to live, and food to eat. If a population grows too fast, it creates very severe difficulties.
6) Unfortunately, it's a very difficult problem to solve — and it's getting rapidly worse.

More People Means More Environmental Damage

1) As these poorer countries gradually become more industrialised and with rapidly growing populations, the demands on the limited resources of the Earth are increasing sharply.
2) Pollution levels are also increasing, as they burn wood and fossil fuels to power their growing economies, and use up their mineral reserves to create material comforts (just like we do, don't forget).
3) And deforestation is as rampant as ever, to make more room for people and their farming. The great rainforests of the world are being destroyed at an alarming rate by the countries which contain them, in order to make room for cattle rearing and their out-of-control human populations.
4) It can't carry on like this forever. Something real bad will happen if it isn't sorted out pretty soon. That's for sure.

Learn the facts first — then you can build your rocket...

It's real scary innit — the way that graph of world population seems to be pointing nearly vertically upwards... tricky. Anyway, you just worry about your Exams instead, and make sure you learn all the grim facts. Three sections — mini-essays for each, till you know it all.

Problems Caused By Farming

Farming Produces a Lot of Food, Which is Great, but...

1) Farming is important to us because it allows us to produce a lot of food from less and less land.
2) These days it has become quite a high-tech industry. Food production is big business.
3) The great advantage of this is a huge variety of top quality foods, all year round, at cheap prices.
4) This is a far cry from Britain 50 years ago when food had to be rationed by the government because there simply wasn't enough for everyone. That's hard to imagine today... but try...

...Intensive Farming Can Destroy the Environment

Modern methods of farming and agriculture give us the ability to produce plenty of food for everyone. But there's a hefty price to pay. One that we're already paying.
Modern Farming methods can damage the world we live in, making it polluted, unattractive and bereft of wildlife. The main effects are:

1) REMOVAL OF HEDGES to make huge great fields for maximum efficiency.
   This destroys the natural habitat of many wild creatures, and can lead to serious soil erosion.
2) Loss of meadowlands full of wild flowers, of natural woodlands and orchards of cherry trees, of rolling fields of grass and flowers, and tree-topped hills and leafy lanes — just swept away in a couple of decades, along with all the natural timeless beauty of rural England.
3) Careless use of FERTILISERS pollutes rivers and lakes, making them green, slimy and horrible.
4) PESTICIDES DISTURB FOOD CHAINS and reduce many insect, bird and mammal populations.
5) INTENSIVE farming of animals such as battery-hens, and crated veal calves is simply indecent.

It *is* possible to farm efficiently and still maintain a healthy and beautiful environment.
But maximum profit and efficiency will have to be compromised, if we are to make our countryside more than just one big industrial food factory, and also to treat our fellow creatures (many of whom we will eventually *eat*) with some basic level of decency and respect and humanity.

DEFORESTATION — The Four Big Problems it Causes...

We have already pretty well deforested OUR COUNTRY. Now many under-developed countries are doing the same. However, there are several serious environmental problems that can occur when they suddenly cut lots of trees down in these tropical climates:

1) DECREASE IN RAINFALL in that area because moisture is no longer evaporating into the air from the trees.
2) SERIOUS SOIL EROSION when it rains heavily because there are no roots to hold it all together.
3) SERIOUS FLOODING because the soil gets washed into the rivers, silts them up, and over they flow...
4) INCREASE IN CO_2 LEVELS in the atmosphere because the trees aren't there to remove it any more.

So much to learn, so little time to learn it...

More environment problems. This stuff can certainly get a bit tedious. At first it can be quite interesting, but then having to make sure you've learnt all those drivelly little details is not. Still, there's worse things in life than a bit of revision. So learn and enjoy. It's the only way.

Problems Caused By Farming

Pesticides and fertilisers are both artificial chemicals which are spread onto farm land in massive quantities every year. The damaging effects of this haven't always been spotted straight away.

Pesticides Disturb Food Chains

1) Pesticides are sprayed onto most crops to kill the various insects that can damage the crops.
2) Unfortunately, they also kill lots of harmless insects such as bees and beetles.
3) This can cause a shortage of food for many insect-eating birds.
4) Pesticides tend to be poisonous and there's always the danger of the poison passing on to other animals (as well as humans).

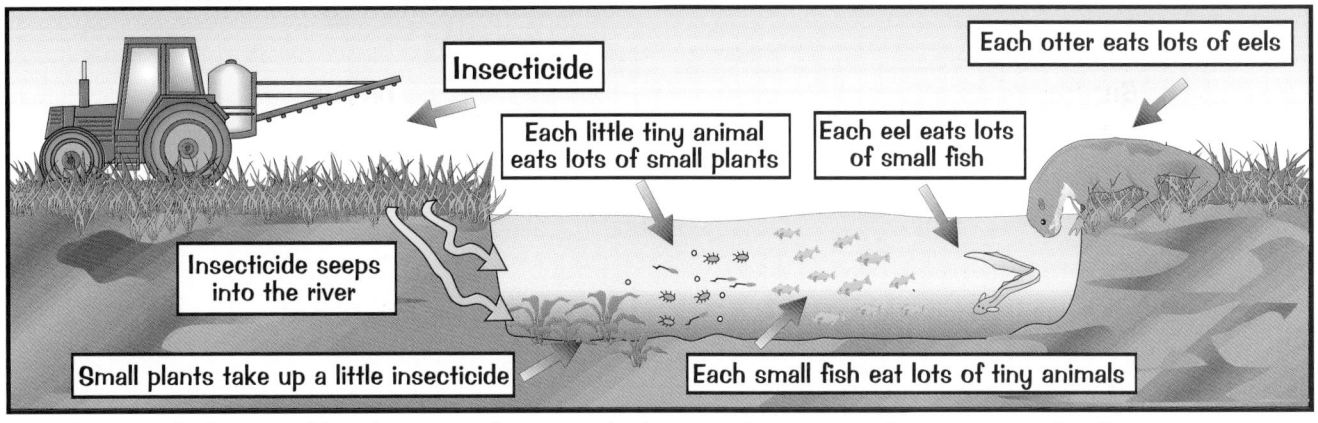

This is well illustrated by the case of otters which were almost wiped out over much of crop-dominated Southern England by a pesticide called DDT in the early 1960s. The diagram shows the food chain which ends with the otter. DDT is not excreted so it accumulates along the food chain and the otter ends up with all the DDT collected by all the other animals.

Fertilisers Damage Lakes and Rivers — by "Mega Death"

1) Fertilisers which contain nitrates are essential to modern farming.
2) Without them crops wouldn't grow nearly so well, and food yields would be well down.
3) This is because the crops take nitrates out of the soil and these nitrates need to be replaced.
4) The problems start if some of the rich fertiliser finds its way into rivers and streams.
5) This happens quite easily if too much fertiliser is applied, especially if it rains soon afterwards.

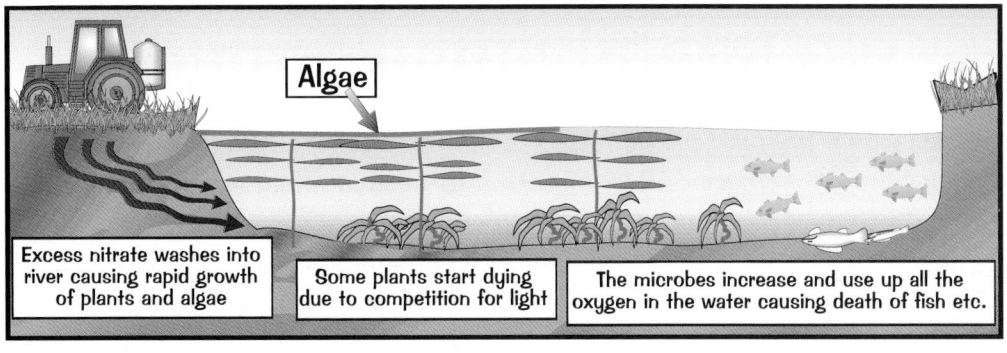

As the picture shows, too many nitrates in the water cause a sequence of "mega-growth", "mega-death" and "mega-decay" involving most of the plant and animal life in the water.

6) Raw sewage pumped into rivers can cause the same problem because the sewage introduces lots of bacteria with "food", and they use up all the oxygen in the water.
7) Farmers need to take a lot more care when spreading artificial fertilisers.

There's nowt wrong wi' just spreading muck on it...

Make sure you distinguish between pesticides (which kill bugs) and fertilisers (which supply nutrients to the plants). They can both cause harm but for totally different reasons. You have to learn the details carefully. Mini-essay time again I'd say. Cover the page and scribble...

Food Webs

A Woodland Food Web

Food webs are pretty easy really. Hideously easy in fact.

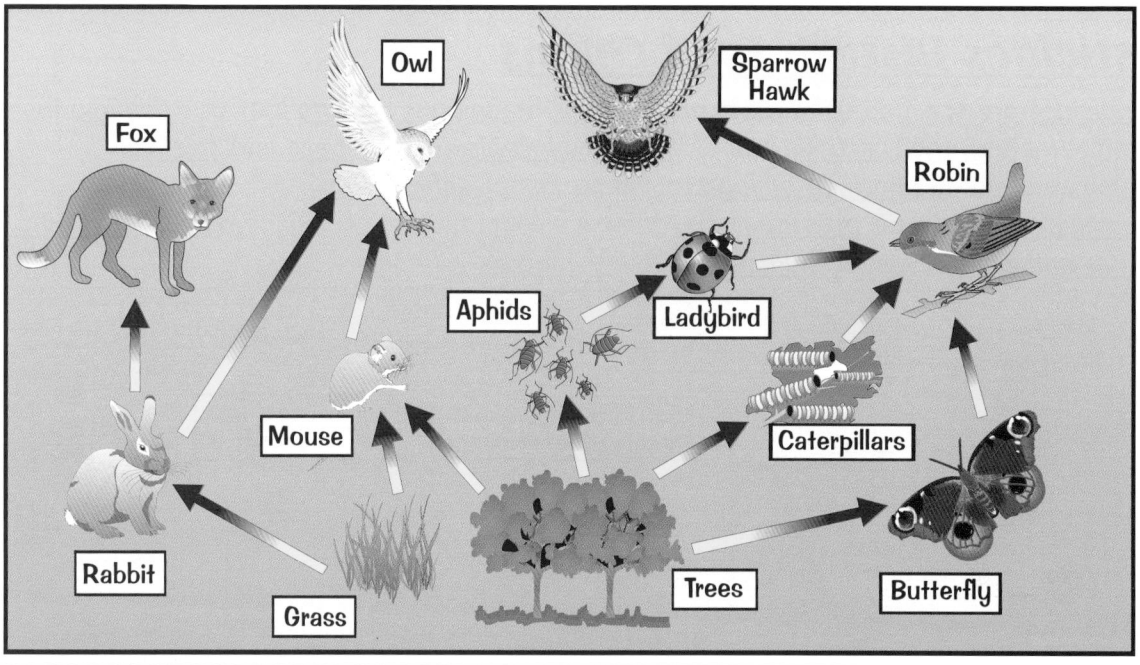

Food Chains — the Arrows show where the Energy goes

1) A *food chain* is just part of a *food web*, starting at the bottom and *following the arrows* up.
2) Remember, the *arrows* show which way the *food energy travels*.
3) Don't mix up *who eats who* either!
   The arrow means "*IS EATEN BY*", so you *follow the arrow* to the one doing the *eating*.
4) From the woodland food web we could take this *food chain*:

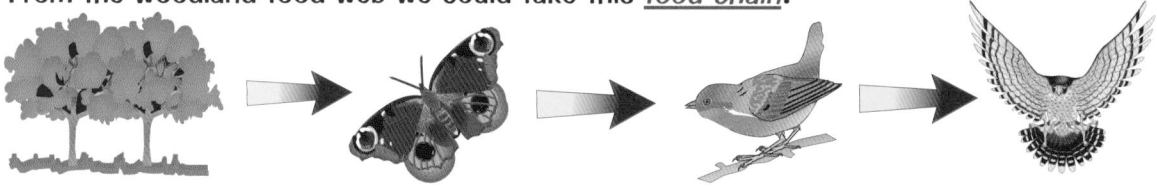

Terminology you need to know

1) *PRODUCER* — all *plants* are *producers*. They use the Sun's energy to produce food energy.
2) *HERBIVORE* — animals which *only eat plants*, e.g. rabbits, caterpillars, aphids.
3) *CONSUMER* — all *animals* are *consumers*. All *plants* are *not*, because they are producers.
4) *PRIMARY CONSUMER* — animal which eats *producers* (plants).
5) *SECONDARY CONSUMER* — animal which eats primary consumers.
6) *TERTIARY CONSUMER* — animal which eats secondary consumers.
7) *CARNIVORE* — eats *only animals*, never plants.
8) *TOP CARNIVORE* — is *not eaten by anything else*, except decomposers after it dies.
9) *OMNIVORE* — eats *both plants and animals*.
10) *DECOMPOSER* — lives off all *dead material* — producers, consumers, top carnivore, the lot.

Learn about Food Webs, terminology and all...

That's got to be the prettiest food web ever drawn, wouldn't you say? Yeah well, anyway, the pretty pictures are the easy bit. It's those *10 definitions* which you really need to work at. That's what'll sort out the sheep from the goats in the Exam. So make sure you *know them all*.

Making Holes in Food Webs

A Typical Food Web for a Pond

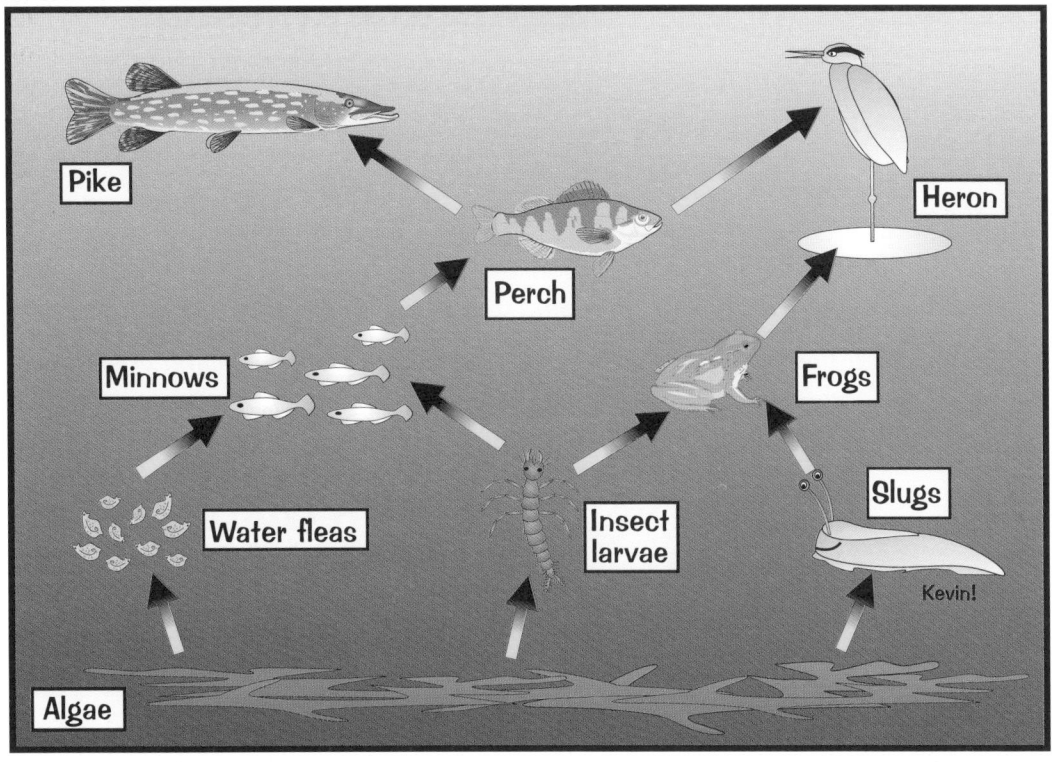

Exam Q. — What happens if you take out the frogs...?

1) This is the *usual Exam question*.
2) One of the animals is *wiped out* — what effect will this have on the *other* creatures?
3) For example, if all the *frogs* were *removed* what'd happen to the number of *slugs* or *perch*?
4) It's *simple enough*, but you do have to *think it through* fairly carefully:
   a) *SLUGS* would *increase* because there'd be *nothing to eat them* now.
   b) *PERCH* is a bit trickier. With no frogs the herons will get *hungry* and so will *eat more perch* (and minnows and insect larvae), so the perch will in fact *decrease* in number.

You just have to understand the diagrams (i.e. who eats who) and think about it *real carefully*. Think about which animals *won't now get eaten*, and which animals *will go hungry*, and work out *what they'll do about it* — and the effect that will have *on all the other things* in the web.

Another Exam Q. — What if you took out the Minnows...?

1) First of all, *water fleas* would *increase*.
2) *Perch* on the other hand would be *really struggling*. They'd get *hungry* for a start, but they'd also get *eaten* a lot more *by pike* and *herons*. Toughsky.
3) *Frogs* would initially *benefit* from *more insect larvae* all to themselves, but would then suffer from *herons* eating *more frogs* due to there being *fewer minnows*.
4) *Slugs* would therefore *benefit* because the *frogs* would be eating more *insect larvae* (instead of slugs) and also *getting eaten* by herons. It's all real simple if you just *think it out*.

Learn about making holes in Food webs...

If they give you a food web question you can bet your very last fruit cake they're gonna want to wipe out one of the creatures and ask you what happens then. Practise with both these food webs by wiping out organisms (only one at a time!) and deciding what'll happen to the others.

Pyramids Of Number and Biomass

This is hideously easy too. Just make sure you know what all the pyramids mean.

Each Level you go up, there's fewer of them...

IN OTHER WORDS, each time you go up one level the number of organisms goes down — A LOT. It takes a lot of food from the level below to keep any one animal alive.
This gives us the good old number pyramid:

A typical pyramid of numbers

This is the basic idea anyway. But there are cases where the pyramid is not a pyramid at all:

Number Pyramids Sometimes Look Wrong

This is a pyramid except for the top layer which goes huge:

This is a pyramid apart from the bottom layer which is way too small:

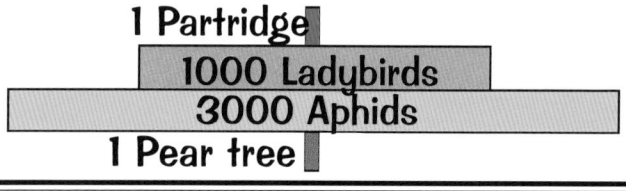

Biomass Pyramids Never Look Wrong

When number pyramids seem to go wrong like this, then the good old PYRAMID OF BIOMASS comes to the rescue. Biomass is just how much all the creatures at each level would "weigh" if you put them all together. So the one pear tree would have a big biomass and the hundreds of fleas would have a very small biomass. Biomass pyramids are ALWAYS the right shape:

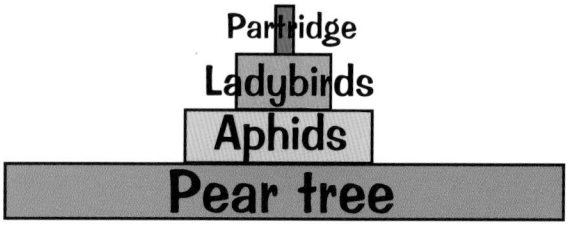

Basically, biomass pyramids are the only sensible way to do it — it's just that number pyramids are easier to understand.

Now Children, get your coloured wooden blocks out...

...hideously easy...

Decomposition and The Carbon Cycle

Another sixties pop group? Sadly not.

1) *Living things* are made of *materials* they take from the world around them.
2) When they *decompose*, ashes are returned to ashes, and dust to dust, as it were.
3) In other words *the elements they contain* are returned to the *soil* where they came from *originally*.
4) These elements are then *used by plants* to grow and the whole cycle *repeats* over and over again.

Decomposition is carried out by Bacteria and Fungi

1) All *plant matter* and *dead animals* are broken down and *decomposed* by *soil bacteria* and *fungi*.
2) This happens everywhere in *nature*, and also in *compost heaps* and *sewage works*.
3) All the important *elements* are thus *recycled*: *Carbon*, *Hydrogen*, *Oxygen* and *Nitrogen*.
4) The *ideal conditions* for creating *compost* are:
   a) ***WARMTH***
   b) ***MOISTURE***
   c) ***OXYGEN (AIR)***
   d) ***DECOMPOSERS*** (i.e. *bacteria* and *fungi*).
   e) ***ORGANIC MATTER*** cut into *small pieces*.

   Make sure you *learn them* — ***ALL FIVE***.

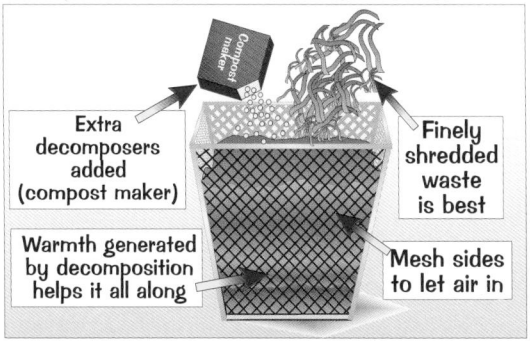

There's a kid I know, and everyone calls him "the party mushroom". I'm not sure why really — they just say he's a fun guy to be with...

The Carbon Cycle Shows how Carbon is Recycled

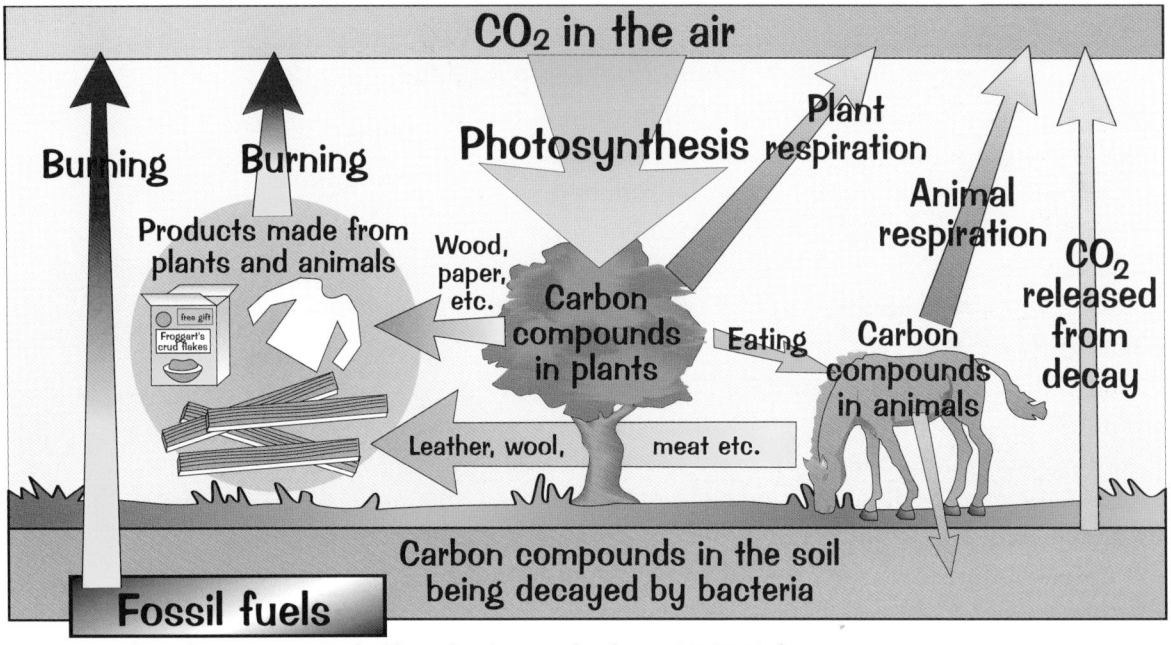

This diagram isn't half as bad as it looks. ***LEARN*** these important points:

1) There's only *one arrow* going ***DOWN***. The whole thing is "powered" by *photosynthesis*.
2) Both plant and animal *respiration* puts CO_2 *back into the atmosphere*.
3) *Plants* convert the carbon in *CO_2 from the air* into *fats*, *carbohydrates* and *proteins*.
4) These can then go *three ways*: *be eaten*, *decay* or be turned into *useful products* by man.
5) *Eating* transfers some of the fats, proteins and carbohydrates to *new* fats, carbohydrates and proteins *in the animal* doing the eating.
6) Ultimately these plant and animal products either *decay* or are *burned* and *CO_2 is released*.

On Ilkley Moor ba 'tat, On Ilkley Moor ba 'tat...

Learn the five ideal conditions for compost making. They like asking about that.
There's another version of the carbon cycle in the Chemistry Book which you really should look at, but this one is easier to understand. Practise *scribbling* it out *from memory*. And *keep trying till you can*.

Revision Summary for Section Five

There's a lot of words in Section Five. Most topics are pretty waffly with a lot of drivelly facts, and it can be real hard to learn them all. But learn them you must. You need to practise scribbling down what you can remember on each topic, and then checking back to see what you missed. These questions give you a pretty good idea of what you should know. You need to practise and practise them — till you can float through them all, like a cloud or something.

1) List seven survival features of the polar bear and of the camel, and five of the cactus plant.
2) Describe in some detail what happens to the populations of prey and predator.
3) Sketch a typical graph of prey and predator populations.
4) Give five survival features for the lion and for the rabbit.
5) What are the *four* basic things which determine the size of a population of a species?
6) What are the three main sources of atmospheric pollution?
7) What are the precise environmental effects of each of these three sources of pollution?
8) What does CFC stand for?
9) Where do CFCs come from? What damage do they do?
10) Which two gases are the biggest cause of the greenhouse effect?
11) Explain how the greenhouse effect happens.
12) What are the two main problems that we expect from the greenhouse effect?
13) What is causing the rise in the level of carbon dioxide in the atmosphere?
14) How can we stop it from increasing still further?
15) What two things are causing the rise in the level of methane in the atmosphere?
16) Which gases cause acid rain? Where do these gases come from?
17) What are the three main harmful effects of acid rain?
18) Explain exactly how fish are killed by acid rain.
19) Give three ways that acid rain can be reduced.
20) What is happening to the world population?
21) What are the two things that are mostly responsible for this trend in population?
22) What can be said about the birth rate and death rate in developing countries?
23) What problems does a rapidly increasing population create for a country?
24) What effect does more and more people have on the environment?
25) What is the great bonus of modern farming methods?
26) What are the main drawbacks of modern farming?
27) What seems to be the most sensible approach now, maybe?
28) List the four problems resulting from deforestation in tropical countries.
29) If deforestation is so bad, why do these countries do it?
30) Why are chemical pesticides used? What are the drawbacks of doing this?
31) Explain in detail how pesticides enter the food chain. What happened with DDT in the '60s?
32) What happens when too much nitrate fertiliser is put onto fields? Give full details.
33) How can this problem with too much nitrate fertiliser be avoided?
34) Describe what food chains and food webs are. Draw a woodland food chain and food web.
35) Draw a food chain and a food web for a pond ecosystem.
36) Write down the 10 technical terms for food webs (P. 84) and give a definition of each one.
37) What is the basic approach to questions which make holes in food webs?
38) What are number pyramids? Why do you generally get a pyramid of numbers?
39) Why do number pyramids sometimes go wrong, and which pyramids are always right?
40) Which two organisms are responsible for the decay of organic matter?
41) What are the five ideal conditions for making compost? Draw a compost maker.
42) What is the Carbon Cycle all to do with? Draw as much of it from memory as you can.

Index

A
a jolly example 2
a nice life 47
a real effort 74
a really boring page 25
a swan or something 18
absorbed 20
ace 22, 72
acid 22
acid gas scrubbers 80
acid rain 78, 80
adaptation 77
addictive 46
aerobic respiration 33
alcohol 34, 46, 47
alcohol-emulsion test 25
allele 60
alligator 55
alveoli, alveolus 31, 32
always take a coat 80
amber 71
amino acids 4, 14, 15, 21, 24, 50
amnion 59
amniotic fluid 59
amphetamine 46
amphibians 54
amylase 21
anaemia 25
anaerobic respiration 34
anchorage 5
animal cells 1
animal characteristics 57
another jolly page 36
antennae 54
anti-rejection drugs 51
antibiotics 45, 46
antibodies 30, 45
antitoxins 30, 45
anus 20
aorta 26, 27, 28
aphids 84, 86
aqueous humour 38
arctic creatures 75
arteries 26, 29
artificial fertilisers 83
artificial selection 68
asexually 63
aspirin 46
atmosphere 87
atmospheric conditions 15
atmospheric pollution 78
atria, atrium 27, 28
auxins 16

B
babies 43
backflow 27
background radiation 64
bacteria 20, 22, 30, 44, 63, 83, 87
balance 35
ball of cells 59
barrier against microbes 44
battery-hens 82
beer 34
beetle 55
Benedict's test 25
bicuspid valve 27, 28
big ears 76
big fancy words 74
big molecules 4, 21, 24
big pink sponges 31
big problems 81
big surface area 4, 5, 9, 23
biomass pyramids 86
birds 54
birth rate 81
Biuret test 25
bladder 50, 58
blind spot 38
block diagram of reflex arc 37
blood 24, 26-29, 30, 50
blood capillaries 59
blood clots 44
blood plasma 40, 48, 51
blood sugar level 41, 49
blood supply 52
blood clotting 30
blood vessels 26, 29, 47
blue budgies 65
body cells 32
body temperature 49, 52, 75
bogs 71
bow legs 25
brain 26, 35, 36, 49
bread 34
breath 51
breathing 31
breathing rate 34
breeding, selective 68
breeds of dog 69
brittle bones 25
bronchi 31
bronchioles 31, 32
bronchitis 47
bronchus 31
bugbears of modern life 78
bugs 83
burning fossil fuels 78

C
cactus 75
calcium 19, 25
camel 75
camouflage 76
cancer 64
canines 22
capillaries 26, 29, 32, 48
carbohydrase 20, 21
carbohydrates 19, 41
carbon 87
Carbon Cycle 87
carbon dioxide 3, 6, 9-13, 32-34, 78-80, 87
carcinogens 64
carnivore 84
carrot plants 14
cars 78, 80
cat 56
catalysts 21
catalytic converters 80
caterpillars 84
cattle rearing 79, 81
cell elongation process 16
cell membranes 1, 4
cell nucleus 60
cell sap 1
cell walls 1, 14
cells 1, 2, 14
cellulose 1, 14
central nervous system 35, 36
cervix 58, 59
CFCs 78
characteristics 64, 68
checkerboard diagram 62
cheeky bee 37
chemical addiction 46
chemical energy 10
chemical messengers 40
chemical stimuli 35
chemicals 64, 83
chewing and grinding 22
chloro-fluoro-carbons 78
chlorophyll 1, 6, 12, 15
chloroplasts 1, 2, 6, 9
chromosomes 60-62, 64, 65
cigarette smoke 64
cilia 44, 47
ciliary muscles, eye 38
circulatory system 26
clean teeth are happy teeth 22
cleaning up emissions 80
clones 17, 56, 63
clot 30, 67
clothes 52
clotting factor, factor 8 67
coal 78
common sense 76
competition 77
compost heaps 87
concentration 3, 4
conjunctiva 38
connector neurone 36
constant internal environment 48
consumer 84
contaminated food 44
continuous variation 57
contraception 81
contraceptive pill 43
Cool? Oh yeah 47
copious blood supply 32
copper sulphate 25
cornea 38
crated veal calves 82
crazy cross-breed 69
creatures 54, 55
cuttings 17
cycle 42
cystic fibrosis 66
cytoplasm 1

D
daffodils 63
dandelions 86
DDT 83
dead cert 9
dead plants or animals 72
death 46
death rate 81
decay 70, 72
decay microbes 71
decomposer 84
decomposition 87
defences 44
deforestation 79, 81, 82
dehydrating 48
dentine 22
deoxygenated blood 26, 27, 29
depressants 46
desert creatures 75
diabetes 41
dialysis 51
diaphragm 31
diet 19
dietary fibre 19
diffusion 3, 4, 32
diffusion of "food" molecules 24
digestive enzymes 21
digestive system 20, 22, 44
dinky little ears 75
dinosaurs 73
dirty water 44

Index

discontinuous variation 57
disease 30, 44, 45, 69, 73
disease-resistance 68, 69
dissolves your teeth 22
DNA molecule 44, 60
double circulatory system 26
double pump 27
Down's Syndrome 65
dragons and stuff 15
drink 51
drivelly facts 88
droop 7
drought 79
drugs 46, 47

E

ears 35
easy peasy 40
ecosystem 77, 80
ecstasy 46
eeek 5
effector 35, 36
effects of environment 57
efficiency 82
egg 42, 43, 54, 58, 59, 61
egg production 40
elastic 29
electrical impulses 36, 37
EM spectrum 64
embryo 59
emissions 80
emphysema 47
enamel 22
enclosed plants 11
endocrine glands 40
energy 10, 14, 33, 34
environment 73, 82
environmental problems 81, 82
environmental variation 56
enzymes 12, 20, 21, 23, 52
epidermis 6
epiglottis 31
equations 9, 10, 33, 34
evaporation 7, 15
every cell in the body 26
evolution 65, 72
excess ions 50
exchange surface 32, 59
exercise 34, 41
exhaust gases 80
extinction 73
extra hair 40
eyes 35, 38

F

faeces 20, 51
fancy word 3, 48
fantastic 47
farming 81-83
fast-moving creatures 26
fats 19, 21, 24, 25
fatty acids and glycerol 21, 24
female hormones 43
female menstrual cycle 42
fermentation 34
Ferrari 47
fertilisation 59, 61, 62
fertilised egg 42, 58
fertilisers 15, 82, 83
fertility treatment 43
filters 50
fingers 49
fish 26, 54, 55, 83
fish, trees and statues 80
fitness and the oxygen debt 34
flaccid 2, 6, 7
fleas 44, 86
flooding 79, 82
flowers 5, 63
flu and colds 45
fluoride 19, 22
flying doughnut 30
focusing 38
foetus 58, 59
fond farewell 20
food 9, 10, 19, 20, 26, 33, 51, 73, 83
food chains 82-84
food energy 84
food for thought 19
food-growing business 17
food tests 25
food webs 84, 85
fossil fuels 78-81
fossils 70, 72, 73
fovea 38
foxes 76, 86
frogs 85
fruits 14, 17
full of pips! 17
fun guy 87
fungi 87

G

gall bladder 20
gamma rays 64
gas exchange 32
genes 56, 60, 64, 67
genetic variation 56
germs 48
get your head round it 74
gills 54
girl or boy? 62
glacier 71
glands 35, 36, 40
glandular tissue 23
glucagon 40, 41
glucose 4, 9, 10, 14, 24, 33, 34, 41
gobble up 30
good clean fun 36
goodness knows 26
gory diagrams 39
Grand Canyon 71
gravity 16
grazers 77
green plants 9
green, slimy and horrible 82
greenhouse effect 78, 79
greenhouses 12
grim looking page 25
grisly bits and bobs 53
grisly stuff 45
growth hormones 16, 17
guard cells 2, 6, 9
gullet 20
gum 22
gut 41

H

haemoglobin 19, 30
haemophilia 67
hairs 52
hairy mammoths 71, 73
hallucinations 46
harmful effects 46
harmless insects 83
healthy growth 15
heart 26, 27
heart attacks and strokes 47
heat 49
hedges 82
hepatic artery 26
herbivores 75, 84
heroin 46
herons 85
hideously easy 84, 86
high concentration 3, 4
high pressure 26, 29
high-tech farming 63, 82
holes in food webs 85
homeostasis 48, 49
hoof 72
hormones 16, 40, 41, 43, 49, 58
horrid flu virus 44, 45
horrid rat flea 44, 45
horse 55, 72
huffing and puffing 31
human chromosomes 61
human reproduction 58
humidity 7
hump 75
Huntington's Chorea 66
hydrochloric acid 20, 44
hydrogen 87

I

identical twins 56, 59
idle creative genius 57
Ilkley Moor 87
immune system 45
implantation 59
in case you didn't know 15
incisors 22
industrial food factory 82
industrialised 81
infinite glory 20
inhaled and exhaled air 33
insects 54, 71
instead of being a sucker 46
insulator 52
insulin 40, 41
intensive farming 82
inter-breeding 69
intercostal muscles 31
internal bleeding 67
iodine 13
iodine test 25
ion content 48
ionising radiation 64
ions 5, 50, 64
iris 38
iron 15, 19, 25, 30
it makes your head hurt 64
it's a nice trick if you can do it 39
it's all clever stuff 24
it's also very long 20

J

jelly 38
jugular vein 26

K

key 55
kidney failure 51
kidney machine 51
kidney transplant 51
kidneys 50
killing weeds 17
kind of clever 4
kinda fizzy 34
kwashiorkor 25

L

lack of 25
lactic acid 34

Index

lakes and rivers 82, 83
large chunk 1
large intestine 20
large surface area 75
larynx 31
lead used in petrol 78
leaf structure 6
leaves 5, 6, 7, 9, 13, 14
lens 38
life processes 1
life's full of little mysteries 26
life's tough 74
light 16
light and dark — the iris 38
light sensitive 38
lignin 8
like a cloud or something 88
limiting factors 77
lion 76
lipase 20, 21
liver 19, 20 49, 50
liver activity 52
low concentration 3, 4
low pressure 26
LSD 46
lumen 29
lung cancer 47
lungs 26, 31, 32, 49

M

magnesium 15
malaria 44, 67
male or female 62
mammals 54
maximum profit 82
mega-death 83
melting of the polar ice-caps 79
menstrual cycle 42, 43, 58
metabolism 41, 52
meteorite 73
methane 79
methedrine 46
microbes 30, 44, 45
middle toe 72
migration 77
mineral reserves 81
minerals 4, 7, 8, 14, 15, 19, 70
minnows 85
missing links 72
mitral valve 27
modern farming 68, 81-83
modern medicine 81
moist lining 32
molars 22
monkeys 80
monoculture 15
morphine 46
mosquitoes 44
motor neurone 35, 36
MRS NERG 1
mucus 23, 44, 66
multiple births 43
murdered 71
muscles 27, 35, 49
muscular tissue 23
mutagens 64
mutations 64, 65

N

natural gas 78
natural habitat 82
natural selection 65
natural timeless beauty 82
NEAB syllabuses only 40, 41
near and distant objects 38
nerve cells 36
nerve fibres 35
nerve impulse 36, 37
nerves 19, 40
neurones 35-37
nicotine 47
nitrates 14, 15, 83
nitrogen 33, 87
nitrogen oxides 80
non-identical twins 59
nose 35
nuclear radiation 64
nucleus 1, 44, 59, 60, 61, 64
number pyramid 86
nutrient deficiencies 25
nutrition 19

O

obliging male 59
obsessive tea-drinking 46
oesophagus 20
oestrogen 40, 43
offspring 62
oil 78
omnivore 84
optic nerve 38
organ systems 2
organic matter 87
organs 2, 49
otters 83
outward characteristics 61
ovaries 40, 43, 58
oviducts 58, 59
oxides of nitrogen 78
oxygen 3, 9, 10, 26, 32, 33, 70, 83, 87
oxygen debt 34
oxygenated blood 26, 27, 29
oxyhaemoglobin 30, 32
ozone layer 78

P

pain killers 46
pain receptor 37
palisade cells 6, 9
palisade layer 6
palisade leaf cells 2
pancreas 20, 40, 41, 49
particularly jolly leaf experiments 13
particularly nasty 46
pear tree 86
penicillin 46
penis 58
perch 85
perforated end-plates 8
perils of monoculture 15
peristalsis 23
pesticides 82, 83
petrification 70
petrol 78
pH 20
phloem tubes 6, 8
photosynthesis 1, 2, 3, 5, 6, 9, 10, 12, 13, 87
physical activity 41
pike 85
pips 17
pituitary gland 40, 49
placenta 59
plant 7
plant cells 1
plant hormones 16, 17
plants 5, 10, 14, 87
plasma 30
platelets 30
pleural fluid 31
poisonous 47, 50, 75, 80, 83
poisons 45
polar bear 75
polar ice-caps 79
pollen 5
pollinate 5, 17, 63
polluted 82
pollution 81
poor countries 81
poor growth 15
population 76, 77
pores 6
potato 14, 63
potometer 15
power stations 78, 80
predators 22, 73, 76, 77
pregnant women 59
premolars 22
pressure 35
pretty serious stuff 74
pretty tough 53
pretty tricky 48
prey 76
primary consumer 84
prizes! 53
probably blatted 73
producer 84
products of digestion 21
progesterone 43
prostate gland 58
protease 20, 21
proteins 4, 14, 15, 19, 21, 24, 25
psychological addiction 46
puberty 40
pulmonary artery/vein 26, 27, 28
pulse and breathing rate 34
pummels 20
pump 27
pumping cycle 28
pupil 38
pyramids 86

Q

quick absorption 23

R

rabbits 76, 84, 86
radiation 64
rainfall 82
rainforests 81
rat flea 45, 46
rate of photosynthesis 12
raw sewage 83
real bad 81
real easy stuff 18
receptors 35
recovery time 34
rectum 20
red blood cells 30, 67
red meat 19
reflexes 36, 37
relay neurone 36
removal of hedges 82
renal artery/vein 26, 50
reproduce 63
reproduction 58, 63
reproductive cells 61
reproductive organs 58
reptiles 54
resistant "strain", bacteria 65
resources 81
respiration 10, 14, 33, 87

Index

respiratory tract 44
responses 37
retina 38
ribcage 31
rice growing 79
rickets 25
ripening hormone 17
rock and soil strata 71
root hairs 4, 5
rooting compound 17, 63
roots 5, 7, 8, 15, 16, 75
rot if you don't 22
roughage 19
ruffian sportsmen 22

S

salivary amylase 20, 71
salivary glands 20
salty meal 50
scrotum 58
scrubbers 80
scurvy 25
sea-levels 79
secondary consumer 84
secondary sexual characteristics 40
sediments 70
seedless grapes 17
seeds 14, 17
selective breeding 68, 69
semen 58
semi-lunar valves 27, 28
seminal vesicle 58
sense organs 35
sensitive 35
sensory neurones 35, 36
serious depression 46
serious learning 17
seriously boring food tests 25
severe downward spiral 47
sewage 83
sewage works 87
sexual characteristics 40
sexual intercourse 44
sheep 1
shivering 49
shoot tips 8, 16
shoots and roots 16
shrivelling up like a prune 19
sickle cell anaemia 67
silly names 21, 29
simple sugars 21, 25
skin 35, 48, 49
skin cancer 78
skin problems like scurvy 25
slimy 54
slugs 85
small intestine 20, 23, 24
smaller molecules 4, 21, 24
smell 35
smoking 47
sodium 19, 50
sodium hydroxide 25
soil 5, 7, 14, 15
soil bacteria and fungi 87
soil erosion 82
soil strata 71
solvents 46
some tough questions 18
sound-receptors 35
spectacularly dumb 18
sperm 58, 59, 61
sperm production 40
sphincters 20, 28, 50
spiders 54
spinal cord 35, 36
spongy layers 6
spreading muck on it 83
starch 4, 6, 8, 14, 21, 24, 25
starch test 13
statues 80
stem 5, 63, 75
sternum 31
stimulants 46
stimuli, stimulus 35
stomach 20, 44
stomata 2, 3, 6, 75
storage organs 8
strawberry 63
strokes 47
strong and stiff 8
stubborn cats notwithstanding 57
stupefyingly easy 73
sucrose 14
suffer 45
sugar 22, 41
sugar content 48
sugars 21
sulphur dioxide 78, 80
Sun 79
sunlight 9
Sun's energy 10, 84
surface area 4, 5, 9, 20, 23, 30, 32, 75
suspensory ligaments 38
sweat, sweating 50, 75
sweat gland 52
swollen roots 14
symptoms 66, 67
synapse 36

T

tadpoles 59
take out the frogs 85
taking the mickey 51
tar 47
target cells 40
taste 35
teeth 22, 76
teeth and bones 19
temperature 12, 48
temperature receptors 35
tertiary consumer 84
testes 40, 58
testicles 58
testosterone 40
the black death 44
the main culprits 78
The Pill 43
there are no marks for being a clot 78
there's no drivel 35
thorax 31
tips 16
tissue fluid 48
tissues 2
tobacco 47
tongue 35
too cold /too hot 52
too many people 81
tooth decay 22
toothpaste 22
top carnivore 84
touch 35
toughsky 25
toxins 30, 44, 45
trachea 31
transpiration 3, 6, 7, 15
transport 8
tricuspid valve 27, 28
turgid 2, 6, 7
turgor pressure 7
twins 56, 59

U

ultra-violet light 64
upbringing 56
urea 48, 50, 51
ureter 50
urethra 58
urine 51
uterus 43, 58, 59
uterus lining 42
UV rays 78

V

vacuole 1
vagina 42, 58, 59
valves 27, 29
variation in plants and animals 56
vasoconstriction 52
vasodilation 52
vectors 44
veins 26, 29
vena cava 26, 27, 28
ventricles 27, 28
vigorous exercise 34, 41
villi 20, 23
viruses 44
vision 76
vitamin C 25
vitamin D 25
vitamins 19
vitreous humour 38
voice box 31

W

waste product 50
wastes 48
water 7-10, 19
water content of blood 48, 50
water fleas 85
water loss 75
water uptake 15
water vapour 3
weedkillers 17
weeds 17
weird smell 3
white blood cells 30, 45
wind pipe 31
wings 54
winter 14
wolves 69
womb 58
world population 81
worries 54
wound 30
wreck your life 47

X

X and Y chromosomes 62
X-chromosome 67
X-rays 64
xylem tubes 6, 8

Y

Y-chromosome 67
yeast 34
yield 15, 68, 69, 83
you're on your own, pal 45

Z

zygote 59, 62